Introduction

Pupils' written work

Abacus textbooks are unique in that they provide clear guidance to pupils on how their work should be recorded. Pupils should be encouraged to follow this guidance, which will make marking their work substantially easier, and clearly focused.

Marking pupils' work

Clearly it is important that pupils' work is seen and checked by the teacher regularly, but it is not necessary for all work to be marked by the teacher. Decisions about which work should be teacher-marked, and how it should be marked will be made alongside the need to maximise time available for teaching and guiding pupils through their activities.

A suggested approach within Abacus is to make these decisions Unit by Unit. Decide, for example, for each Unit, which parts you want to mark, and which parts the pupils can mark.

Marking the 'Explores'

The 'Explores' should generally be marked by the teacher. The 'Explores' often require a systematic approach, and the answers give suggestions for these. These approaches can be communicated to the pupils, to help them develop systematic ways of working. Also, the pupils' responses to the 'Explores' may well vary because of the often open-ended nature of the activities.

For many 'Explores' you may want to ask the pupils to work in pairs or groups, possibly leading to a group display of the results of their 'exploration'.

Contents

Number Textbook 1

page 3

Place-value **N1**

4-digit numbers

1. £3000, £600, £80, £1
2. £6000, £600, £90, £9
3. £1000, £200, £70, £9
4. £1000, £800, £50, £5
5. £4000, £500, £30, £7
6. £4000, £500, £7
7. £2000, £10, £6
8. £7000, £100, £10
9. £3000, £800, £5

Numbers in order £1279 £1855 £2016 £3681 £3805 £4507 £4537 £6699 £7110

10. 2764
11. 4229
12. 5993
13. 8644
14. 1117
15. 5082
16. 7960
17. 1406
18. 4720

Numbers in order 1117 1406 2764 4229 4720 5082 5993 7690 8644

e 1117 1279 1406 1855 2016 2764 3681 3805 4229
4507 4537 4720 5082 5993 6699 7110 7960 8644

---

page 4

Place-value **N1**

4-digit numbers

1. 700
2. 500
3. 70
4. 4000
5. 600
6. 9
7. 2000
8. 70
9. 900
10. 1

Train numbers in order 2803 3772 3972 4013 4768 6690 6960 7241 8561 9999

e Answers will vary.

Explore

11. 2003, 2005, 2060, 2063, 2065, 2090, 2093, 2095, 2100, 2103, 2105, 2160, 2163, 2165, 2190, 2193, 2195
12. 2700, 2703, 2705, 2760, 2763, 2765, 2790, 2793, 2795
13. 3003, 3005, 3060, 3063, 3065, 3090, 3093, 3095, 3100, 3103, 3105, 3160, 3163, 3165, 3190, 3193, 3195
14. 3700, 3703, 3705, 3760, 3763, 3765, 3790, 3793, 3795

Number Textbook 1

page 5

Place-value **N1**

4-digit numbers

1. 1213 < 1867 Blues won by 654 points
2. 1975 > 1933 Reds won by 42 points
3. 2410 > 2230 Reds won by 180 points
4. 3014 < 3118 Blues won by 104 points
5. 3667 < 3676 Blues won by 9 points
6. 4110 > 4100 Reds won by 10 points
7. 5568 < 5881 Blues won by 313 points
8. 6314 > 5999 Reds won by 315 points
9. 8006 < 8600 Blues won by 594 points

See answers above.

10. 3890 > 3880
11. 4230 > 4130 (or 4030)
12. 3156 < 3166 (or 3176, 3186, 3196)
13. 2899 < 2903 (or 2913, 2923, 2933, 2943, 2953, 2963, 2973, 2983, 2993)
14. 3052 > 3042 (or 3032, 3022, 3012, 3002)
15. 4548 < 4549, 4640 (or 4641, … 4649), 4740 (or 4741, … 4749), 4840 (or 4841, … 4849), 4940 (or 4941, … 4949)
16. (8309, 8319, 8329, 8339 or) 8349 < 8350 (or 8351, 8352, 8353, 8354, 8355, 8356, 8357, 8358, 8359)

---

page 6

Place-value **N1**

4-digit numbers

1. 4392 **2.** 1584 **3.** 5136 **4.** 8744 **5.** 9220
6. 3500 **7.** 2890 **8.** 6030

Numbers in order 1584 2890 3500 4392 5136 6030 8744 9220

9. Five thousand, two hundred and seventy-one miles
10. Eight thousand, three hundred and forty-three miles
11. Two thousand, five hundred and seventy miles
12. Six thousand, six hundred and ninety-four miles
13. Five thousand, one hundred and forty miles
14. Two thousand, six hundred and three miles
15. Three thousand, three hundred and seventeen miles

9. 5281 miles **10.** 8353 miles **11.** 2580 miles **12.** 6704 miles
13. 5150 miles **14.** 2613 miles **15.** 3327 miles

Number Textbook 1

page 7

Addition/subtraction **N2**

Adding to 10

1. 8 + 2 = 10
2. 4 + 6 = 10
3. 9 + 1 = 10
4. 3 + 7 = 10
5. 0 + 10 = 10
6. 4 + 6 = 10
7. 5 + 5 = 10
8. 7 + 3 = 10
9. 1 + 9 = 10
10. 2 + 8 = 10

11. 8p + 12p = 20p
12. 5p + 15p = 20p
13. 4p + 16p = 20p
14. 1p + 19p = 20p
15. 7p + 13p = 20p
16. 2p + 18p = 20p
17. 6p + 14p = 20p

Explore

Answers will vary.

---

page 8

Addition/subtraction **N2**

Adding to the next ten

1. 28 + 2 = 30
2. 42 + 8 = 50
3. 54 + 6 = 60
4. 17 + 3 = 20
5. 11 + 9 = 20
6. 75 + 5 = 80
7. 66 + 4 = 70
8. 83 + 7 = 90
9. 59 + 1 = 60

10. 43 + 7 = 50
11. 66 + 4 = 70
12. 5 + 15 = 20
13. 38 + 2 = 40
14. 8 + 92 = 100
15. 54 + 6 = 60
16. 3 + 27 = 30
17. 5 + 75 = 80
18. 61 + 9 = 70
19. 41 + 9 = 50

---

page 9

Addition/subtraction **N3**

Adding to the next ten

1. £24 + £6 = £30, £6 more
2. £42 + £8 = £50, £8 more
3. £58 + £2 = £60, £2 more
4. £17 + £3 = £20, £3 more
5. £73 + £7 = £80, £7 more
6. £36 + £4 = £40, £4 more
7. £45 + £5 = £50, £5 more
8. £63 + £7 = £70, £7 more
9. £94 + £6 = £100, £6 more
10. £88 + £2 = £90, £2 more
11. £29 + £1 = £30, £1 more
12. £51 + £9 = £60, £9 more

13. Jane: 63 + 7 = 70 she must borrow 7p
14. Timo: 74 – 12 = 62 62 + 8 = 70 he must save 8p
15. Matthew: 73 + 7 = 80 song was 7 minutes long

Number Textbook 1

page 10

Addition/subtraction **N3**

Finding the difference

1. $135 - 128 = 7$
2. $234 - 226 = 8$
3. $181 - 173 = 8$
4. $163 - 157 = 6$
5. $305 - 299 = 6$
6. $501 - 492 = 9$

$92 - 76 = 16$ cm	up 16 cm from Monday to Tuesday
$104 - 92 = 12$ cm	up 12 cm from Tuesday to Wednesday
$110 - 104 = 6$ cm	up 6 cm from Wednesday to Thursday
$111 - 110 = 1$ cm	up 1 cm from Thursday to Friday
$122 - 111 = 11$ cm	up 11 cm from Friday to Saturday
$134 - 122 = 12$ cm	up 12 cm from Saturday to Sunday

---

page 11

Addition/subtraction **N3**

Finding the difference

1. $226 - 217 = 9$
2. $184 - 178 = 6$
3. $232 - 226 = 6$
4. $151 - 144 = 7$
5. $253 - 247 = 6$
6. $333 - 326 = 7$
7. $125 - 116 = 9$

Answers will vary.

Shahid	$130 - 122 = 8$	Jane	$140 - 136 = 4$
Tim	$140 - 133 = 7$	Jobe	$150 - 142 = 8$
Yasmin	$150 - 141 = 9$	Mel	$150 - 146 = 4$

---

page 12

Addition/subtraction **N3**

Finding the difference

1. $136 - 128 = 8$
2. $223 - 215 = 8$
3. $243 - 237 = 6$
4. $355 - 348 = 7$
5. $192 - 188 = 4$
6. $273 - 266 = 7$
7. $383 - 376 = 7$
8. $452 - 447 = 5$
9. $333 - 325 = 8$

10. $123 + 8 = 131$ $131 - 125 = 6$ 6 stickers left
11. $240 - 224 = 16$ 16 stickers

Number Textbook 1

page 13

Adding pairs to 100 and 1000

Table 1
Pairs to 100

0 + 100 = 100
5 + 95 = 100
10 + 90 = 100
15 + 85 = 100
20 + 80 = 100
25 + 75 = 100
30 + 70 = 100
35 + 65 = 100
40 + 60 = 100
45 + 55 = 100
50 + 50 = 100
55 + 45 = 100
60 + 40 = 100
65 + 35 = 100
70 + 30 = 100
75 + 25 = 100
80 + 20 = 100
85 + 15 = 100
90 + 10 = 100
95 + 5 = 100
100 + 0 = 100

Table 2
Pairs to 1000

0 + 1000 = 1000
50 + 950 = 1000
100 + 900 = 1000
150 + 850 = 1000
200 + 800 = 1000
250 + 750 = 1000
300 + 700 = 1000
350 + 650 = 1000
400 + 600 = 1000
450 + 550 = 1000
500 + 500 = 1000
550 + 450 = 1000
600 + 400 = 1000
650 + 350 = 1000
700 + 300 = 1000
750 + 250 = 1000
800 + 200 = 1000
850 + 150 = 1000
900 + 100 = 1000
950 + 50 = 1000
1000 + 0 = 1000

The numbers in Table 2 are all 10 times the numbers in Table 1.

a 45, 55 **b** 95, 5 **c** 40, 60 **d** 35, 65 **e** 75, 25
f 15, 85 **g** 20, 80 **h** 10, 90 **i** 65, 35 **j** 85, 15
k 70, 30 **l** 55, 45

Number Textbook 1

page 14

Addition/subtraction **N4**

Adding pairs to 100 and 1000

1. 350 + 650 = 1000 ml
2. 250 + 750 = 1000 ml
3. 150 + 850 = 1000 ml
4. 550 + 450 = 1000 ml
5. 400 + 600 = 1000 ml
6. 650 + 350 = 1000 ml
7. 200 + 800 = 1000 ml
8. 450 + 550 = 1000 ml

9. £85 **10.** £45 **11.** £64 **12.** £28 **13.** £81

---

page 15

Addition/subtraction **N4**

Adding pairs to 100

60 + 40 = 100 kg
68 + 32 = 100 kg
55 + 45 = 100 kg
26 + 74 = 100 kg
49 + 51 = 100 kg

Explore

Any of the following:

13, 87	14, 86	16, 84	17, 83	21, 79	24, 76	26, 74
29, 71	31, 69	32, 68	38, 62	39, 61	41, 59	42, 58
43, 57	47, 53	48, 52	49, 51			

---

page 16

Addition/subtraction **N5**

Adding several numbers

1. £7 + £3 + £11 + £8 = £29
2. £8 + £8 + £3 + £12 = £31
3. £13 + £13 + £7 + £7 + £9 = £49
4. £13 + £7 + £4 + £4 = £28
5. £12 + £2 + £6 + £13 = £33
6. £6 + £6 + £2 + £2 + £4 = £20
7. £11 + £7 + £3 + £9 = £30
8. £11 + £6 + £9 + £3 = £29
9. £3 + £3 + £12 + £2 + £2 + £8 = £30
10. £7 + £7 + £8 + £6 = £28

e Answers will vary.

11. 4 + 7 + 8 + 9 = 28
12. 8 + 6 + 5 + 4 = 23
13. 6 + 12 + 6 + 7 = 31
14. 13 + 9 + 7 + 8 = 37
15. 11 + 8 + 9 + 12 = 40
16. 4 + 8 + 6 + 2 + 9 = 29
17. 13 + 11 + 9 + 7 = 40
18. 15 + 3 + 5 + 8 + 7 = 38

Number Textbook 1

page 17

Addition/subtraction **N5**

Adding several numbers

1. 6 + 4 + 8 + 5 + 3 = 26
2. 9 + 2 + 4 + 8 = 23
3. 5 + 9 + 6 + 8 = 28
4. 3 + 7 + 9 + 2 + 4 = 25
5. 3 + 5 + 8 + 12 = 28
6. 3 + 5 + 7 + 11 + 8 = 34
7. 5 + 9 + 6 + 8 + 12 = 40
8. 3 + 7 + 11 + 2 + 8 = 31
9. Answers will vary.

---

page 18

Addition/subtraction **N5**

Adding several numbers

1. 5 + 3 + 4 + 9 + 8 = 29
2. 10 + 5 + 3 + 8 + 7 = 33
3. 6 + 9 + 8 + 4 + 9 = 36
4. 7 + 9 + 11 + 3 + 8 = 38
5. 9 + 8 + 9 + 2 + 8 = 36
6. 9 + 6 + 8 + 5 + 8 = 36
7. 5 + 3 + 14 + 5 + 6 = 33
8. 4 + 7 + 12 + 9 + 8 = 40
9. 9 + 11 + 9 + 6 + 6 = 41

Explore

2 + 8 + 9 = 19, 2 + 8 + 3 + 6 = 19, 2 + 8 + 4 + 5 = 19, 3 + 7 + 9 = 19,
3 + 7 + 4 + 5 = 19, 4 + 6 + 9 = 19, 4 + 6 + 2 + 7 = 19, 4 + 7 + 8 = 19,
5 + 6 + 8 = 19, 2 + 3 + 5 + 9 = 19

---

page 19

Addition/subtraction **N5**

Adding several numbers

1. 12 + 9 + 7 + 8 + 7 = 43
2. 11 + 10 + 8 + 7 + 6 = 42
3. 6 + 4 + 9 + 10 + 10 = 39
4. 3 + 3 + 8 + 5 + 9 = 28
5. 8 + 4 + 2 + 8 + 7 = 29
6. 6 + 11 + 10 + 4 + 3 = 34
7. 7 + 7 + 14 + 10 + 7 = 45
8. 5 + 4 + 10 + 11 + 9 = 39

Cost of names: answers will vary.

e Answers will vary.

Number Textbook 1

page 20

Properties of number **N6**

Counting in 1s, 25s and 50s

1. 347, 348, 349
2. 228, 229, 230
3. 409, 410, 411
4. 666, 667, 668
5. 398, 399, 400
6. 800, 801, 802
7. 849, 850, 851
8. 309, 310, 311
9. 99, 100, 101
10. 554, 555, 556
11. 737, 738, 739
12. 915, 916, 917

● 1. 338, 348, 358
2. 219, 229, 239
3. 400, 410, 420
4. 657, 667, 677
5. 389, 399, 409
6. 791, 801, 811
7. 840, 850, 860
8. 300, 310, 320
9. 90, 100, 110
10. 545, 555, 565
11. 728, 738, 748
12. 906, 916, 926

13. 200, 250, 300
14. 175, 200, 225
15. 375, 400, 425
16. 250, 275, 300
17. 750, 800, 850
18. 1050, 1100, 1150

---

page 21

Properties of number **N6**

Counting in 25s and 50s

1. £4·50 + 50p = £5·00
2. 30p + 50p = 80p
3. £1·10 + 50p = £1·60
4. £2·20 + 50p = £2·70
5. £3·40 + 50p = £3·90
6. £6·50 + 50p = £7·00
7. £2·00 + 50p = £2·50
8. £5·20 + 50p = £5·70
9. £7·00 + 50p = £7·50
10. £4·40 + 50p = £4·90
11. £9·30 + 50p = £9·80
12. £8·50 + 50p = £9·00
13. £7·10 + 50p = £7·60

14. 600, 550, 500
15. 225, 200, 175
16. 825, 800, 175
17. 850, 800, 750
18. 500, 450, 400
19. 275, 250, 225

---

page 22

Properties of number **N6**

Counting in 25s and 50s

1. 763, 813, 863, 913
2. 192, 242, 292, 342, 392, 442, 492
3. 518, 568, 618, 668, 718, 768, 818
4. 360, 310, 260, 210, 160, 110, 60
5. 474, 524, 574, 624, 674, 724, 774
6. 1180, 1130, 1080, 1030, 980, 930, 880

Explore

0 to 1000 in 25s: would write 20 numbers ending in 5
1000 to 2000 in 25s: would write 20 numbers ending in 5

Number Textbook 1

page 23

Multiplying

1. 2 x 4 = 8 **2.** 3 x 2 = 6 **3** 4 x 4 = 16 **4.** 3 x 3 = 9

Neil and Ella	4 x 5 = 5 x 4
Kate and Jane	2 x 6 = 6 x 2
Bec and Amos	3 x 5 = 5 x 3
Mike and Carlos	2 x 8 = 8 x 2
Habeeb and Samira	3 x 6 = 6 x 3
Jo and Bob	4 x 6 = 6 x 4

---

page 24

Multiplying

1. 2 x 5 = 10, 5 x 2 = 10
2. 3 x 5 = 15, 5 x 3 = 15
3. 3 x 7 = 21, 7 x 3 = 21
4. 4 x 2 = 8, 2 x 4 = 8

5. 2 x 9 = 18, 9 x 2 = 18 and 3 x 6 = 18, 6 x 3 = 18
6. 2 x 6 = 12, 6 x 2 = 12 and 4 x 3 = 12, 3 x 4 = 12
7. 2 x 12 = 24, 12 x 2 = 24 and 3 x 8 = 24, 8 x 3 = 24
   (or 4 x 6 = 24, 6 x 4 = 24)
8. 2 x 8 = 16, 8 x 2 = 16 and 4 x 4 = 16

9.	8 x 2 = 16	2 x 8 = 16	**10.**	3 x 4 = 12	4 x 3 = 12
11.	2 x 5 = 10	5 x 2 = 10	**12.**	6 x 3 = 18	3 x 6 = 18
13.	3 x 10 = 30	10 x 3 = 30	**14.**	7 x 2 = 14	2 x 7 = 14
15.	9 x 5 = 45	5 x 9 = 45	**16.**	1 x 6 = 6	6 x 1 = 6
17.	8 x 3 = 24	3 x 8 = 24	**18.**	9 x 2 = 18	2 x 9 = 18
19.	5 x 4 = 20	4 x 5 = 20	**20.**	6 x 4 = 24	4 x 6 = 24

---

page 25

Multiplying

1. 4 x 45p = 180p = £1·80
2. 2 x 55p = 110p = £1·10
3. 3 x 60p = 180p = £1·80
4. 3 x 45p = 135p = £1·35
5. 4 x 35p = 140p = £1·40
6. 5 x 45p = 225p = £2·25
7. 3 x 55p = 165p = £1·65
8. 5 x 60p = 300p = £3·00
9. 4 x 55p = 220p = £2·20

e

Screamer	11 turns (£4·95)
Dipper	9 turns (£4·95)
Big Wish	8 turns (£4·80)
Water Splash	14 turns (£4·90)

page 25 cont ...

Multiplication/division N7

Explore

24: 1 x 24 = 24, 24 x 1 = 24
2 x 12 = 24, 12 x 2 = 24
3 x 8 = 24, 8 x 3 = 24
4 x 6 = 24, 6 x 4 = 24 4 pairs

18: 1 x 18 = 18, 18 x 1 = 18
2 x 9 = 18, 9 x 2 = 18
3 x 6 = 18, 6 x 3 = 18 3 pairs

60: 1 x 60 = 60, 60 x 1 = 60
2 x 30 = 60, 30 x 2 = 60
3 x 20 = 60, 20 x 3 = 60
4 x 15 = 60, 15 x 4 = 60
5 x 12 = 60, 12 x 5 = 60
6 x 10 = 60, 10 x 6 = 60 6 pairs

---

page 26

Multiplication/division N7

Multiplying

1. 20 x 3 m = 3 m x 20 = 60 m
2. 30 x 2 m = 2 m x 30 = 60 m
3. 31 x 5 m = 5 m x 31 = 155 m
4. 25 x 6 m = 6 m x 25 = 150 m
5. 38 x $\frac{1}{2}$ m = $\frac{1}{2}$ m x 38 = 19 m
6. 35 x 4 m = 4 m x 35 = 140 m

e **1.** 120 m **2.** 80 m **3.** 200 m **4.** 240 m **5.** 20 m **6.** 160 m

7. 4 x 60p = 240p = £2·40 £2·40 – £2·00 = 40p needs 40p more
8. 3 x 40p = 120p = £1·20 2 x 50p = 100p = £1·00
£1·20 + £1·00 = £2·20 total cost £2·20
9. 5 x 40 cm = 200 cm 3 m = 300 cm 300 cm – 200 cm = 100 cm 1 m left
10. 5 x 30p = 150p = £1·50 £2·00 – £1·50 = 50p 50p change

---

page 27

Multiplication/division N8

Dividing

1. 18 ÷ 3 = 6 (or 18 ÷ 6 = 3)
2. 12 ÷ 3 = 4 (or 12 ÷ 4 = 3)
3. 16 ÷ 2 = 8 (or 16 ÷ 8 = 2)
4. 15 ÷ 5 = 3 (or 15 ÷ 3 = 5)
5. 28 ÷ 4 = 7 (or 28 ÷ 7 = 4)
6. 30 ÷ 5 = 6 (or 30 ÷ 6 = 5)
7. 40 ÷ 5 = 8 (or 40 ÷ 8 = 5)
8. 21 ÷ 3 = 7 (or 21 ÷ 7 = 3)
9. 12 ÷ 4 = 3 (or 12 ÷ 3 = 4)
10. 27 ÷ 3 = 9 (or 27 ÷ 9 = 3)

11. 20 ÷ 4 = 5 **12.** 30 ÷ 3 = 10 **13.** 14 ÷ 2 = 7 **14.** 16 ÷ 4 = 4
15. 28 ÷ 7 = 4 **16.** 18 ÷ 2 = 9 **17.** 16 ÷ 2 = 8 **18.** 12 ÷ 6 = 2
19. 20 ÷ 5 = 4 **20.** 30 ÷ 10 = 3 **21.** 25 ÷ 5 = 5 **22.** 24 ÷ 6 = 4

Number Textbook 1

page 28

Multiplication/division N8

Dividing

1. 18 ÷ 3 = 6
2. 30 ÷ 3 = 10
3. 15 ÷ 3 = 5
4. 24 ÷ 3 = 8
5. 21 ÷ 3 = 7
6. 33 ÷ 3 = 11
7. 36 ÷ 3 = 12
8. 27 ÷ 3 = 9
9. 39 ÷ 3 = 13

10. 25 ÷ 5 = 5
11. 40 ÷ 5 = 8
12. 24 ÷ 4 = 6
13. 28 ÷ 4 = 7
14. 30 ÷ 10 = 3
15. 60 ÷ 6 = 10
16. 14 ÷ 2 = 7
17. 60 ÷ 5 = 12
18. 24 ÷ 3 = 8
19. 36 ÷ 4 = 9
20. 27 ÷ 3 = 9

---

page 29

Multiplication/division N8

Dividing

1. 20 ÷ 4 = 5
2. 32 ÷ 4 = 8
3. 40 ÷ 4 = 10
4. 28 ÷ 4 = 7
5. 16 ÷ 4 = 4
6. 48 ÷ 4 = 12

7. 40 ÷ 5 = 8
8. 90 ÷ 10 = 9
9. 10 ÷ 2 = 5
10. 16 ÷ 4 = 4
11. 20 ÷ 5 = 4
12. 21 ÷ 3 = 7
13. 24 ÷ 6 = 4
14. 30 ÷ 5 = 6
15. 36 ÷ 6 = 6
16. 24 ÷ 2 = 12

Explore

36 ÷ 1 = 36 36 ÷ 2 = 18 36 ÷ 3 = 12 36 ÷ 4 = 9 36 ÷ 6 = 6
36 ÷ 9 = 4 36 ÷ 12 = 3 36 ÷ 18 = 2 36 ÷ 36 = 1
9 pairs

---

page 30

Multiplication/division N8

Dividing

1. 35 cm ÷ 5 = 7 cm
2. 27 cm ÷ 3 = 9 cm
3. 44 cm ÷ 2 = 22 cm
4. 36 cm ÷ 6 = 6 cm
5. 32 cm ÷ 4 = 8 cm
6. 66 cm ÷ 2 = 33 cm
7. 110 cm ÷ 10 = 11 cm
8. 21 cm ÷ 3 = 7 cm
9. 45 cm ÷ 5 = 9 cm
10. 54 cm ÷ 6 = 9 cm

Total of 46 pieces

11. 24 ÷ 4 = 6 — 6 cats
12. 3 x 9 = 27 — 27 + 2 = 29 — 29 biscuits
13. 40 ÷ 5 = 8 — 8 piles
14. £36 ÷ 4 = £9 — £9 each
    4 x £10 = £40 — £40 – £36 = £4 need £4 more

Number Textbook 1

page 31

Multiplication/division **N9**

Multiplying

1. a 6 **b** 16 **2. c** 15 **d** 35
3. e 8 **f** 16 **g** 36 **4. h** 30 **i** 60
5. j 12 **k** 18 **l** 27

6. 3 x 4 = 12 **7.** 2 x 5 = 10 **8.** 4 x 10 = 40
9. 6 x 3 = 18 **10.** 4 x 4 = 16 **11.** 3 x 3 = 9
12. 8 x 5 = 40 **13.** 9 x 3 = 27 **14.** 8 x 2 = 16
15. 7 x 4 = 28 **16.** 5 x 2 = 10 **17.** 10 x 5 = 50
18. 7 x 3 = 21

---

page 32

Multiplication/division **N9**

Multiplying and dividing

1. 8, 12, 16, 24, 28, 32, 36, 40
2. 9, 12, 15, 18, 21, 24, 27, 30, 36, 42
3. 12, 24, 36
4. 14, 22

5. 8 ÷ 2 = 4 **6.** 12 ÷ 3 = 4 **7.** 5 x 4 = 20 **8.** 40 ÷ 10 = 4
9. 25 ÷ 5 = 5 **10.** 7 x 5 = 35 **11.** 32 ÷ 4 = 8 **12.** 9 x 3 = 27
13. 18 ÷ 2 = 9 **14.** 21 ÷ 3 = 7

---

page 33

Multiplication/division **N9**

Multiplying and dividing

1. 4 x 4 = 16 **2.** 18 ÷ 3 = 6 **3.** 5 x 4 = 20 **4.** 7 x 3 = 21
5. 20 ÷ 4 = 5 **6.** 9 x 3 = 27 **7.** 28 ÷ 4 = 7 **8.** 8 x 3 = 24
9. 35 ÷ 5 = 7 **10.** 3 x 4 = 12

11. 6, 12, 18, 24, 30, 36, 42, 48, 54, 60
12. 12, 24, 36, 48, 60 **13.** 15, 30, 45, 60
14. 20, 40, 60 **15.** 30, 60
16. 10, 20, 30, 40, 50, 60 **17.** 20, 40, 60
18. 4, 8, 12, 16, 20, 24, 28, 32, 36, 40, 44, 48, 52, 56, 60

e Answers will vary.

Number Textbook 1

page 34

Doubling and halving

1. double 18 = 20 + 16 = 36
2. double 37 = 60 + 14 = 74
3. double 48 = 80 + 16 = 96
4. double 26 = 40 + 12 = 52
5. double 29 = 40 + 18 = 58
6. double 46 = 80 + 12 = 92
7. double 27 = 40 + 14 = 54
8. double 57 = 100 + 14 = 114
9. double 38 = 60 + 16 = 76
10. double 36 = 60 + 12 = 72

11. half of 12 = 6
12. half of 16 = 8
13. half of 20 = 10
14. half of 30 = 15
15. half of 18 = 9
16. half of 24 = 12
17. half of 42 = 21
18. half of 64 = 32
19. half of 32 = 16
20. half of 80 = 40
21. half of 60 = 30
22. half of 48 = 24
23. half of 88 = 44

11. 3 **12.** 4 **13.** 5 **14.** $7\frac{1}{2}$ **15.** $4\frac{1}{2}$ **16.** 6 **17.** $10\frac{1}{2}$ **18.** 16 **19.** 8 **20.** 20 **21.** 15 **22.** 12 **23.** 22

---

page 35

Doubling

1. 2 x 23p = 46p
2. 2 x 42p = 84p
3. 2 x 31p = 62p
4. 2 x 18p = 36p
5. 2 x 25p = 50p
6. 2 x 13p = 26p
7. 2 x 35p = 70p
8. 2 x 47p = 94p
9. 2 x 28p = 56p
10. 2 x 22p = 44p
11. 2 x 33p = 66p
12. 2 x 29p = 58p
13. 2 x 44p = 88p

14.

in	20	50	70	90	60	30	80	40
out	40	100	140	180	120	60	160	80

15.

in	15	55	75	45	25	85	35	65
out	30	110	150	90	50	170	70	130

Number Textbook 1

page 36

Multiplication/division **N10**

Doubling and halving

1. double 23 + 24 = 46 + 24 = 70
2. double 25 + 28 = 50 + 28 = 78
3. 26 + double 21 = 26 + 42 = 68
4. double 26 + double 24 = 52 + 48 = 100
5. double 34 + 31 = 68 + 31 = 99
6. 32 + double 33 = 32 + 66 = 98
7. 39 + double 33 = 39 + 66 = 105
8. 27 + double 43 = 27 + 86 = 113
9. double 34 + 42 = 68 + 42 = 110
10. double 26 + double 43 = 52 + 86 = 138

❷	first board:	double 28 + double 28 = 56 + 56 = 112
	second board:	double 39 + double 39 = 78 + 78 = 156
	third board:	double 43 + double 43 = 86 + 86 = 172

Explore

23 pairs, using each card only once

96, 48	92, 46	90, 45	86, 43	82, 41	78, 39
76, 38	72, 36	70, 35	68, 34	64, 32	62, 31
58, 29	56, 28	54, 27	46, 23	38, 19	36, 18
34, 17	32, 16	30, 15	28, 14	26, 13	

---

page 37

Multiplication/division **N11**

Fours and eights

	x4	x8	❷ (x16)
1.	2 x 4 = 8	2 x 8 = 16	2 x 16 = 32
2.	3 x 4 = 12	3 x 8 = 24	3 x 16 = 48
3.	4 x 4 = 16	4 x 8 = 32	4 x 16 = 64
4.	5 x 4 = 20	5 x 8 = 40	5 x 16 = 80
5.	6 x 4 = 24	6 x 8 = 48	6 x 16 = 96
6.	7 x 4 = 28	7 x 8 = 56	7 x 16 = 112

1. 3 x 8 = 24 **2.** 2 x 8 = 16 **3.** 5 x 8 = 40 **4.** 4 x 8 = 32
5. 1 x 8 = 8 **6.** 10 x 8 = 80 **7.** 8 x 8 = 64 **8.** 6 x 8 = 48
9. 9 x 8 = 72

❷ **1.** 12 **2.** 8 **3.** 20 **4.** 16 **5.** 4 **6.** 40 **7.** 32 **8.** 24 **9.** 36

Number Textbook 1

page 38

Multiplication/division **N11**

Fours and eights

1. 8, 12, 16, 20, 24, 28, 32, 36, 40
2. 8, 16, 24, 32, 40
3. 8, 16, 24, 32, 40
4. 14, 18, 22, 26, 30

Answers will vary.

5. 24 ÷ 8 = 3	**6.** 40 ÷ 8 = 5	**7.** 8 ÷ 8 = 1	**8.** 48 ÷ 8 = 6
9. 16 ÷ 8 = 2	**10.** 80 ÷ 8 = 10	**11.** 64 ÷ 8 = 8	**12.** 32 ÷ 8 = 4
13. 56 ÷ 8 = 7	**14.** 72 ÷ 8 = 9		

---

page 39

Multiplication/division **N11**

Fours and eights

1. double 40 = 80	10 x 8 = 80	**2.** double 24 = 48	6 x 8 = 48
3. double 52 = 104	13 x 8 = 104	**4.** double 60 = 120	15 x 8 = 120
5. double 32 = 64	8 x 8 = 64	**6.** double 48 = 96	12 x 8 = 96
7. double 80 = 160	20 x 8 = 160	**8.** double 44 = 88	11 x 8 = 88
9. double 400 = 800	100 x 8 = 800	**10.** double 36 = 72	9 x 8 = 72
11. double 120 = 240	30 x 8 = 240	**12.** double 200 = 400	50 x 8 = 400

Answers will vary.

Explore

Pattern of units digits in x4 table: 4, 8, 2, 6, 0, 4, 8, …
Pattern of units digits in x8 table: 8, 6, 4, 2, 0, 8, …

---

page 40

Multiplication/division **N11**

Fours and eights

1. 3 x 8p = 24p	**2.** 5 x 8p = 40p	**3.** 7 x 8p = 56p	**4.** 10 x 8p = 80p
5. 6 x 8p = 48p	**6.** 4 x 8p = 32p	**7.** 8 x 8p = 64p	**8.** 40p ÷ 8p = 5
9. 56p ÷ 8p = 7	**10.** 24p ÷ 8p = 3	**11.** 64p ÷ 8p = 8	**12.** 80p ÷ 8p = 10

13. 7 x 8 = 56	60 – 56 = 4	7 teams, 4 children left over
14. 7 x 8 = 56	56 people	
15. 12 x 8 = 96	100 – 96 = 4	12 stamps, 4p change
16. 48 cm ÷ 8 = 6 cm		each side 6 cm long

Number Textbook 1

page 41
Fractions/decimals N12

Fractions

1. $\frac{6}{8}$ 2. $\frac{2}{4}$ 3. $\frac{1}{3}$ 4. $\frac{1}{4}$ 5. $\frac{4}{6}$ 6. $\frac{2}{3}$ 7. $\frac{3}{5}$ 8. $\frac{5}{6}$ 9. $\frac{3}{6}$ 10. $\frac{5}{8}$

11. green $\frac{3}{5}$, yellow $\frac{2}{5}$ 12. green $\frac{2}{8}$, yellow $\frac{6}{8}$ 13. green $\frac{5}{9}$, yellow $\frac{4}{9}$
14. green $\frac{2}{6}$, yellow $\frac{4}{6}$ 15. green $\frac{4}{8}$, yellow $\frac{4}{8}$ 16. green $\frac{1}{7}$, yellow $\frac{6}{7}$
17. green $\frac{5}{10}$, yellow $\frac{5}{10}$

---

page 42
Fractions/decimals N12

Fractions

1. $2\frac{2}{5}$ 2. $1\frac{3}{4}$ 3. $3\frac{1}{2}$ 4. $2\frac{2}{3}$ 5. $1\frac{5}{6}$ 6. $2\frac{3}{8}$ 7. $3\frac{2}{6}$

❷ 1. $2\frac{3}{5}$ 2. $3\frac{1}{4}$ 3. $1\frac{1}{2}$ 4. $2\frac{1}{3}$ 5. $3\frac{1}{6}$ 6. $2\frac{5}{8}$ 7. $1\frac{4}{6}$
8. $3\frac{2}{5}$ 9. $1\frac{3}{4}$ 10. $4\frac{1}{3}$ 11. $2\frac{1}{2}$ 12. $2\frac{6}{8}$ 13. $3\frac{3}{4}$ 14. $1\frac{2}{6}$

❷ 8. $1\frac{3}{5}$ 9. $2\frac{1}{4}$ 10. $1\frac{2}{3}$ 11. $2\frac{1}{2}$ 12. $1\frac{2}{8}$ 13. $2\frac{1}{4}$ 14. $3\frac{4}{6}$

---

page 43
Fractions/decimals N12

Fractions

1. $1\frac{1}{4}$ hours 2. $1\frac{3}{4}$ hours 3. $\frac{3}{4}$ hour 4. 2 hours 5. $1\frac{1}{2}$ hours
6. $2\frac{1}{4}$ hours 7. $3\frac{1}{4}$ hours 8. $1\frac{1}{3}$ km 9. $2\frac{1}{3}$ km 10. $1\frac{2}{3}$ km
11. $3\frac{1}{3}$ km 12. 1 km 13. 3 km 14. 4 km 15. $3\frac{2}{3}$ km
16. $5\frac{2}{3}$ km

---

page 44
Fractions/decimals N13

Matching fractions

1. $\frac{1}{2} = \frac{2}{4}$ 2. $\frac{3}{4} = \frac{6}{8}$, $\frac{1}{4} = \frac{2}{8}$ 3. $\frac{2}{6} = \frac{1}{3}$, $\frac{4}{6} = \frac{2}{3}$ 4. $\frac{2}{3} = \frac{4}{6}$, $\frac{1}{3} = \frac{2}{6}$
5. $\frac{1}{3} = \frac{3}{9}$, $\frac{2}{3} = \frac{6}{9}$ 6. $\frac{2}{4} = \frac{4}{8}$ 7. $\frac{2}{8} = \frac{1}{4}$, $\frac{6}{8} = \frac{3}{4}$
8. $\frac{2}{4} = \frac{1}{2}$ 9. $\frac{2}{8} = \frac{1}{4}$ 10. $\frac{2}{2}$ = 1 whole 11. $\frac{4}{8} = \frac{2}{4}$
12. $\frac{4}{8} = \frac{1}{2}$ 13. $\frac{4}{4}$ = 1 whole 14. $\frac{6}{8} = \frac{3}{4}$ 15. $\frac{8}{8}$ = 1 whole

---

page 45
Fractions/decimals N13

Matching fractions

1. $\frac{1}{4} = \frac{2}{8}$ 2. $\frac{3}{4} = \frac{6}{8}$ 3. $\frac{1}{3} = \frac{2}{6}$ 4. $\frac{2}{3} = \frac{4}{6}$ 5. $\frac{1}{5} = \frac{2}{10}$ 6. $\frac{4}{5} = \frac{8}{10}$

❷ Answers will vary.

7. $\frac{2}{6} = \frac{1}{3}$ 8. $\frac{4}{6} = \frac{2}{3}$ 9. $\frac{3}{6} = \frac{1}{2}$ 10. $\frac{3}{3}$ = 1 whole 11. $\frac{6}{6}$ = 1 whole

Number Textbook 1

page 46

Fractions/decimals **N13**

Matching fractions

1. $\frac{4}{10}$ **2.** $\frac{5}{10}$ **3.** $\frac{3}{10}$ **4.** $\frac{6}{10}$ **5.** $\frac{2}{10}$

6. $\frac{2}{6}$ **7.** $\frac{3}{6}$ **8.** $\frac{1}{6}$ **9.** $\frac{4}{6}$

$\frac{4}{10} = \frac{2}{5}$ $\frac{5}{10} = \frac{1}{2}$ $\frac{6}{10} = \frac{3}{5}$ $\frac{2}{10} = \frac{1}{5}$ $\frac{2}{6} = \frac{1}{3}$ $\frac{3}{6} = \frac{1}{2}$ $\frac{4}{6} = \frac{2}{3}$

Explore

$\frac{1}{2} = \frac{3}{6}$ $\frac{1}{2} = \frac{4}{8}$ $\frac{1}{2} = \frac{5}{10}$ $\frac{1}{3} = \frac{2}{6}$ $\frac{1}{4} = \frac{2}{8}$ $\frac{1}{5} = \frac{2}{10}$

$\frac{2}{3} = \frac{4}{6}$ $\frac{2}{3} = \frac{6}{9}$ $\frac{2}{5} = \frac{4}{10}$ $\frac{3}{4} = \frac{6}{8}$ $\frac{3}{5} = \frac{6}{10}$ $\frac{4}{5} = \frac{8}{10}$

12 pairs

---

page 47

Addition/subtraction **N14**

Adding near multiples of 10

1. 4 + 30 = 34 **2.** 17 + 19 = 36 **3.** 23 + 29 =52 **4.** 38 + 29 = 67
5. 45 + 29 = 74 **6.** 52 + 39 = 91 **7.** 66 + 19 = 85 **8.** 79 + 21 = 100
9. 81 + 11 = 92 **10.** 94 + 39 = 133

+	36	25	42	30	18	6	54	21
19	55	44	61	49	37	25	73	40
21	57	46	63	51	39	27	75	42
39	75	64	81	69	57	45	93	60

36 + 59 = 95 25 + 59 = 84 42 + 59 = 101 30 + 59 = 89
18 + 59 = 77 6 + 59 = 65 54 + 59 = 113 21 + 59 = 80

---

page 48

Addition/subtraction **N14**

Adding and subtracting near multiples of 10

1. 14 + 32 = 46 **2.** 27 + 32 = 59 **3.** 38 + 32 = 70 **4.** 46 + 32 = 78
5. 54 + 32 = 86 **6.** 67 + 32 = 99 **7.** 75 + 32 = 107 **8.** 81 + 32 = 113
9. 93 + 32 = 125 **10.** 98 + 32 = 130

11. 45 – 29 = 16 **12.** 48 – 29 = 19 **13.** 51 – 29 = 22 **14.** 57 – 29 = 28
15. 64 – 29 = 35 **16.** 69 – 29 = 40 **17.** 73 – 29 = 44 **18.** 86 – 29 = 57
19. 92 – 29 = 63 **19a.** 95 – 29 = 66

20. 275 – 29 = 246 **21.** 432 – 29 = 403 **22.** 556 + 39 = 595
23. 674 – 39 = 635 **24.** 783 – 49 = 734 **25.** 326 + 49 = 375
26. 245 – 39 = 206

Number Textbook 1

page 49

Addition/subtraction N14

Adding near multiples of 10

1. 45p + 39p = 84p 2. 53p + 39p = 92p 3. 28p + 39p = 67p
4. 38p + 39p = 77p 5. 35p + 39p = 74p 6. 47p + 39p = 86p
7. 58p + 39p = 97p 8. 69p + 39p = 108p = £1·08

1. 45p – 11p = 34p 2. 53p – 11p = 42p 3. 28p – 11p = 17p
4. 38p – 11p = 27p 5. 35p – 11p = 24p 6. 47p – 11p = 36p
7. 58p – 11p = 47p 8. 69p – 11p = 58p

Explore

Many different possible answers e.g. 39 + 49 + 59 + 89 = 236 (tens and/or hundreds digits must add to 200)

---

page 50

Addition/subtraction 

Subtracting near multiples of 10

1. 132 – 29 = 103 2. 246 – 29 = 217 3. 381 – 29 = 352
4. 163 – 29 = 134 5. 154 – 29 = 125 6. 443 – 29 = 414
7. 262 – 29 = 233 8. 191 – 29 = 162 9. 285 – 29 = 256

10. 67p – 39p = 28p 28p + 50p = 78p has 78p now
11. 82 + 19 + 29 = 130 minutes watched TV for 130 minutes
12. £42 – £19 = £23 £23 + £32 = £55 has £55 now

---

page 51

Addition/subtraction 

Adding multiples of 10

1. 24 + 13 = 37 240 + 130 = 370 2. 16 + 12 = 28 160 + 120 = 280
3. 17 + 5 = 22 170 + 50 = 220 4. 25 + 8 = 33 250 + 80 = 330
5. 23 + 24 = 47 230 + 240 = 470 6. 13 + 9 = 22 130 + 90 = 220
7. 34 + 6 = 40 340 + 60 = 400 8. 15 + 7 = 22 150 + 70 = 220
9. 42 + 21 = 63 420 + 210 = 630 10. 63 + 14 = 77 630 + 140 = 770

Answers will vary.

11. 230 + 140 = 370 cm 12. 310 + 140 = 450 cm
13. 210 + 140 = 350 cm 14. 420 + 140 = 560 cm
15. 360 + 140 = 500 cm 16. 750 + 140 = 890 cm
17. 860 + 140 = 1000 cm

Number Textbook 1

page 52

Addition/subtraction N15

Adding multiples of 10

1. 4 + 7 = 11 | 40 + 70 = 110 | 400 + 700 = 1100
2. 8 + 6 = 14 | 80 + 60 = 140 | 800 + 600 = 1400
3. 3 + 12 = 15 | 30 + 120 = 150 | 300 + 1200 = 1500
4. 16 + 7 = 23 | 160 + 70 = 230 | 1600 + 700 = 2300
5. 9 + 15 = 24 | 90 + 150 = 240 | 900 + 1500 = 2400
6. 13 + 9 = 22 | 130 + 90 = 220 | 1300 + 900 = 2200
7. 14 + 11 = 25 | 140 + 110 = 250 | 1400 + 1100 = 2500
8. 22 + 14 = 36 | 220 + 140 = 360 | 2200 + 1400 = 3600
9. 7 + 17 = 24 | 70 + 170 = 240 | 700 + 1700 = 2400
10. 9 + 19 = 28 | 90 + 190 = 280 | 900 + 1900 = 2800

11. £140 + £50 = £190
12. £230 + £50 = £280
13. £310 + £50 = £360
14. £440 + £50 = £490

e **11.** £310 **12.** £220 **13.** £140 **14.** £10

---

page 53

Addition/subtraction N15

Subtracting multiples of 10

1. 13 – 7 = 6 | 130 – 70 = 60
2. 18 – 9 = 9 | 180 – 90 = 90
3. 24 – 8 = 16 | 240 – 80 = 160
4. 21 – 6 = 15 | 210 – 60 = 150
5. 34 – 7 = 27 | 340 – 70 = 270
6. 23 – 12 = 11 | 230 – 120 = 110
7. 36 – 8 = 28 | 360 – 80 = 280
8. 42 – 9 = 33 | 420 – 90 = 330
9. 27 – 13 = 14 | 270 – 130 = 140
10. 63 – 9 = 54 | 630 – 90 = 540
11. 540 – 110 = 430
12. 170 – 80 = 90
13. 210 – 110 = 100
14. 1200 – 700 = 500 cm
15. 1500 – 700 = 800 cm
16. 2100 – 700 = 1400 cm
17. 2400 – 700 = 1700 cm

e **14.** 500 – 400 = 100 cm
15. 800 – 400 = 400 cm
16. 1400 – 400 = 1000 cm
17. 1700 – 400 = 1300 cm

---

page 54

Addition/subtraction 

Subtracting multiples of 10

1. 23 – 12 = 11 | 230 – 120 = 110 | 2300 – 1200 = 1100
2. 32 – 6 = 26 | 320 – 60 = 260 | 3200 – 600 = 2600
3. 28 – 7 = 21 | 280 – 70 = 210 | 2800 – 700 = 2100
4. 21 – 9 = 12 | 210 – 90 = 120 | 2100 – 900 = 1200
5. 17 – 11 = 6 | 170 – 110 = 60 | 1700 – 1100 = 600
6. 16 – 8 = 8 | 160 – 80 = 80 | 1600 – 800 = 800
7. 34 – 12 = 22 | 340 – 120 = 220 | 3400 – 1200 = 2200

page 54 cont ...

Addition/subtraction 

8. 45 – 9 = 36   450 – 90 = 360   4500 – 900 = 3600
9. 53 – 11 = 42   530 – 110 = 420   5300 – 1100 = 4200
10. 49 – 13 = 36   490 – 130 = 360   4900 – 1300 = 3600

@ 600 + 800 + 2200 + 3600 + 4200 + 3600 = 15000

11. 80 + 30 + 20 = 130   page 130
12. £270 + £80 = £350   £350 – £150 = £200   £200 left

---

page 55

Place-value N16

4-digit numbers

1. 2317, 2318, 2319
2. 4240, 4241, 4242
3. 3108, 3109, 3110
4. 5446, 5456, 5466
5. 4730, 4740, 4750
6. 3200, 3210, 3220
7. 4416, 4516, 4616
8. 8004, 8104, 8204
9. 2179, 2279, 2379
10. 4825, 5825, 6825
11. 5167, 6167, 7167
12. 4006, 5006, 6006

@
1. 2315, 2314, 2313
2. 4238, 4237, 4236
3. 3106, 3105, 3104
4. 5426, 5416, 5406
5. 4710, 4700, 4690
6. 3180, 3170, 3160
7. 4216, 4116, 4016
8. 7804, 7704, 7604
9. 1979, 1879, 1779
10. 2825, 1825, 825
11. 3167, 2167, 1167
12. 2006, 1006, 6

13. 2349
14. 3426
15. 2474
16. 2650
17. 3090
18. 4099
19. 2799
20. 3116

---

page 56

Place-value N16

4-digit numbers

1. 33
2. 113
3. 344
4. 578, 589
5. 251
6. 392
7. 317
8. 536, 646
9. 660, 770
10. 430, 440

11. 1974
12. 1502
13. 581
14. 1076
15. 1818
16. 1600
17. 1676
18. 1339
19. 2009

@ 581, 1076, 1339, 1502, 1600, 1676, 1818, 1974, 2009

---

page 57

Place-value N16

3-digit and 4-digit numbers

1. 2256 km
2. 4782 km
3. 3445 km
4. 7234 km
5. 5904 km
6. 6149 km
7. 2973 km
8. 9420 km
9. 9330 km
10. 5051 km
11. 4410 km
12. 1143 km

Number Textbook 1

page 57 cont ...

Place-value N16

Distances in order
1143 km, 2256 km, 2973 km, 3445 km, 4410 km, 4782 km, 5051 km, 5904 km, 6149 km, 7234 km, 9330 km, 9420 km

Explore
Answers will vary.

---

page 58

Addition/subtraction N17

Adding several 2-digit numbers

1. 26 + 37 + 25 = 88
2. 19 + 63 + 25 = 107
3. 24 + 86 + 25 = 135
4. 33 + 72 + 25 = 130
5. 38 + 74 + 25 = 137
6. 43 + 55 + 25 = 123
7. 46 + 68 + 25 = 139

8. 35 + 43 + 25 = 103
9. 62 + 17 + 25 = 104
10. 42 + 25 + 37 = 104
11. 51 + 19 + 26 = 96
12. 38 + 42 + 16 = 96
13. 24 + 32 + 28 = 84
14. 35 + 28 + 17 = 80
15. 43 + 22 + 18 = 83

---

page 59

Addition/subtraction N17

Adding several 2-digit numbers

1. 32p + 29p + 22p = 83p
2. 27p + 34p + 17p = 78p
3. 38p + 36p + 25p = 99p
4. 36p + 22p + 17p = 75p
5. 34p + 22p + 36p = 92p
6. 29p + 27p + 38p = 94p
7. 32p + 17p + 38p = 87p

Answers will vary.

8. 35 + 45 + 17 = 97
9. 96 + 4 + 18 = 118
10. 42 + 37 + 19 = 98
11. 52 + 25 + 18 = 95
12. 43 + 34 + 25 = 102
13. 27 + 28 + 29 = 84
14. 48 + 45 + 35 = 128
15. 28 + 38 + 48 = 114

---

page 60

Addition/subtraction

Adding several 2-digit numbers

1. 27 + 36 + 42 = 105
2. 29 + 35 + 44 = 108
3. 27 + 35 + 44 = 106 or 42 + 29 + 35 = 106
4. 27 + 29 + 35 = 91
5. 27 + 36 + 44 = 107 or 36 + 42 + 29 = 107
6. 27 + 29 + 44 = 100 or 36 + 29 + 35 = 100
7. 42 + 35 + 44 = 121
8. 27 + 36 + 29 = 92
9. 42 + 29 + 44 = 115 or 36 + 35 + 44 = 115
10. 27 + 36 + 35 = 98 or 27 + 42 + 29 = 98

page 60 cont ...

Addition/subtraction N17

◉ 104, 113, 122, 109

27 + 42 + 35 = 104
27 + 42 + 44 = 113 or 36 + 42 + 35 = 113
36 + 42 + 44 = 122
36 + 29 + 44 = 109

11. 72 + 32 + 47 = 151 page 151
12. £48 + £22 + £27 = £97 she has £97

---

page 61

Addition/subtraction N17

Adding several 2-digit numbers

1. 27 + 15 + 13 = 55 km
2. 24 + 8 + 26 = 58 km
3. 23 + 26 + 15 = 64 km
4. 24 + 9 + 23 = 56 km
5. 24 + 13 + 12 = 49 km
6. 22 + 13 + 15 = 50 km
7. 12 + 24 + 22 = 58 km
8. 13 + 22 + 9 = 44 km

Explore
Various answers possible, e.g. a = 2, b = 4, c = 1, d = 7, e = 6 (24 + 21 + 17 = 62)

---

page 62

Addition/subtraction N18

Adding multiples of 10

1. 342 + 40 = 382
2. 725 + 30 = 755
3. 551 + 40 = 591
4. 329 + 50 = 379
5. 218 + 70 = 288
6. 424 + 70 = 494
7. 643 + 40 = 683
8. 183 + 10 = 193
9. 325 + 70 = 395
10. 469 + 30 = 499

11. £445 + £50 = £495
12. £225 + £50 = £275
13. £342 + £50 = £392
14. £236 + £50 = £286
15. £320 + £50 = £370
16. £516 + £50 = £566

---

page 63

Addition/subtraction N18

Adding multiples of 10

1. 216 + 80 = 296 m
2. 325 + 70 = 395 m
3. 248 + 50 = 298 m
4. 139 + 70 = 209 m
5. 314 + 90 = 404 m
6. 527 + 40 = 567 m
7. 243 + 80 = 323 m
8. 128 + 90 = 218 m
9. 417 + 50 = 467 m

◉ **1.** 496 m **2.** 595 m **3.** 498 m **4.** 409 m **5.** 604 m **6.** 767 m
7. 523 m **8.** 418 m **9.** 667 m

page 63 cont ...

Addition/subtraction N18

Explore

16 additions

415 + 90 = 505
410 + 95 = 505
425 + 80 = 505
420 + 85 = 505
435 + 70 = 505
430 + 75 = 505
445 + 60 = 505
440 + 65 = 505
465 + 40 = 505
460 + 45 = 505
475 + 30 = 505
470 + 35 = 505
485 + 20 = 505
480 + 25 = 505
495 + 10 = 505
490 + 15 = 505

---

page 64

Addition/subtraction N18

Adding multiples of 10 and 100

1. £117 + £160 = £277
2. £239 + £160 = £399
3. £406 + £160 = £566
4. £319 + £160 = £479
5. £224 + £160 = £384
6. £133 + £160 = £293
7. £253 + £160 = £413
8. £111 + £160 = £271
9. £142 + £160 = £302
10. 358 + 20 + 30 = 408   408 runs
11. 421 + 40 + 20 = 481   481 runs
12. 451 + 30 + 10 = 491   491 runs

---

page 65

Addition/subtraction 

Subtracting 2-digit numbers

1. 43 – 27 = 16
2. 42 – 18 = 24
3. 72 – 38 = 34
4. 61 – 25 = 36
5. 54 – 17 = 37
6. 64 – 27 = 37
7. 44 – 26 = 18
8. 56 – 38 = 18
9. 62 – 25 = 37
10. 73 – 28 = 45
11. 51 – 25 = 26
12. 82 – 38 = 44
13. 84 – 36 = 48
14. 75 – 17 = 58
15. 43 – 25 = 18
16. 53 – 24 = 29
17. 64 – 28 = 36
18. 74 – 38 = 36

---

page 66

Addition/subtraction N19

Subtracting 2-digit numbers

1. 82 – 53 = 29
2. 82 – 66 = 16
3. 82 – 35 = 47
4. 82 – 58 = 24
5. 82 – 48 = 34
6. 82 – 37 = 45
7. 82 – 45 = 37
8. 82 – 27 = 55
9. 82 – 64 = 18
10. 82 – 55 = 27
11. 82 – 25 = 57
12. 82 – 63 = 19

page 66 cont ...

Addition/subtraction N19

Explore

80, 55   71, 46   96, 71   62, 37   87, 62   53, 28   78, 53
44, 19   69, 44   35, 10   60, 35   51, 26   42, 17
(other 3- and 4-digit numbers possible)

---

page 67

Addition/subtraction N19

Subtracting 2-digit numbers

1. 92 – 78 = 14 minutes
2. 84 – 58 = 26 minutes
3. 92 – 38 = 54 minutes
4. 104 – 86 = 18 minutes
5. 94 – 62 = 32 minutes
6. 112 – 92 = 20 minutes
7. 86 – 67 = 19 minutes
8. 125 – 91 = 34 minutes
9. 110 – 64 = 46 minutes
10. 98 – 66 = 32 minutes

e
1. 92 + 78 = 170 minutes
2. 84 + 58 = 142 minutes
3. 92 + 38 = 130 minutes
4. 104 + 86 = 190 minutes
5. 94 + 62 = 156 minutes
6. 112 + 92 = 204 minutes
7. 86 + 67 = 153 minutes
8. 125 + 91 = 216 minutes
9. 110 + 64 = 174 minutes
10. 98 + 66 = 164 minutes

11. 83 – 47 = 36
12. 61 – 28 = 33
13. 52 – 18 = 34
14. 72 – 37 = 35
15. 92 – 45 = 47
16. 64 – 26 = 38
17. 55 – 18 = 37
18. 73 – 25 = 48
19. 87 – 36 = 51
20. 94 – 27 = 67

---

page 68

Addition/subtraction N20

Subtracting 2-digit numbers

1. 63 – 35 = 28
2. 72 – 25 = 47
3. 81 – 43 = 38
4. 93 – 38 = 55
5. 65 – 28 = 37
6. 73 – 37 = 36
7. 82 – 45 = 37
8. 54 – 28 = 26
9. 64 – 17 = 47
10. 51 – 23 = 28

11. 63 – 8 = 55
12. 72 – 7 = 65
13. 54 – 8 = 46
14. 41 – 7 = 34
15. 33 – 8 = 25
16. 62 – 7 = 55
17. 91 – 8 = 83
18. 42 – 5 = 37
19. 34 – 8 = 26
20. 63 – 7 = 56

21. 72 – 29 = 43
22. 54 – 19 = 35
23. 61 – 39 = 22
24. 75 – 49 = 26
25. 37 – 19 = 18
26. 64 – 49 = 15
27. 71 – 29 = 42
28. 66 – 29 = 37
29. 55 – 39 = 16
30. 46 – 19 = 27

Number Textbook 1

page 69

Addition/subtraction N20

Subtracting 2-digit numbers

1. 53 – 35 = 18 seconds
2. 62 – 25 = 37 seconds
3. 81 – 36 = 45 seconds
4. 74 – 39 = 35 seconds
5. 64 – 37 = 27 seconds
6. 44 – 19 = 25 seconds
7. 34 – 29 = 5 seconds

- 1. 53 + 35 = 88 seconds
  2. 62 + 25 = 87 seconds
  3. 81 + 36 = 117 seconds
  4. 74 + 39 = 113 seconds
  5. 64 + 37 = 101 seconds
  6. 44 + 19 = 63 seconds
  7. 34 + 29 = 63 seconds

8. 72 – 45 = 27
9. 68 – 45 = 23
10. 92 – 45 = 47
11. 73 – 45 = 28
12. 62 – 45 = 17
13. 58 – 45 = 13

---

page 70

Addition/subtraction N20

Subtracting 2-digit numbers

1. 91 – 68 = 23 cm
2. 45 – 29 = 16 cm
3. 93 – 64 = 29 cm
4. 42 – 18 = 24 cm
5. 51 – 29 = 22 cm
6. 33 – 8 = 25 cm
7. 88 – 75 = 13 cm

8. 62 – 37 = 25 25 km to go
9. 42 – 15 = 27 missed 27 minutes
10. 125 – 82 = 43 needs 43 g more

---

page 71

Addition/subtraction N20

Subtracting 2-digit numbers

1. 74 – 58 = 16 km
2. 91 – 59 = 32 km
3. 82 – 6 = 76 km
4. 74 – 35 = 39 km
5. 66 – 29 = 37 km
6. 72 – 8 = 64 km
7. 38 – 16 = 22 km
8. 90 – 49 = 41 km
9. 75 – 39 = 36 km
10. 46 – 9 = 37 km

- 1. 74 + 58 = 132 km
  2. 91 + 59 = 150 km
  3. 82 + 6 = 88 km
  4. 74 + 35 = 109 km
  5. 66 + 29 = 95 km
  6. 72 + 8 = 80 km
  7. 38 + 16 = 54 km
  8. 90 + 49 = 139 km
  9. 75 + 39 = 114 km
  10. 46 + 9 = 55 km

page 71 cont ...

Explore

Possible amounts:

[Gareth, Dave]	46p, 1p	47p, 2p	48p, 3p	49p, 4p	50p, 5p
51p, 6p	52p, 7p	53p, 8p	54p, 9p	55p, 10p	56p, 11p
57p, 12p	58p, 13p	59p, 14p	60p, 15p	61p, 16p	62p, 17p
63p, 18p	64p, 19p	65p, 20p	66p, 21p	67p, 22p	68p, 23p
69p, 24p	70p, 25p	71p, 26p	72p, 27p		

page 72

Mixed problems

1. Clockwise cycle returns to original number. All the operations combined are the same as performing one operation of multiplying by 10. Crossing off the last digit of a number multiplied by 10 (0) will always leave the original digit.
2. £6 + £19 = £25
   £25 – £5 = £20
   £20 + £10 = £30
   £30 – £8 = £22
   £22 ÷ 2 = £11
   They have £11 each.
3. Mystery number is 34.

Number Textbook 2

page 3

Properties of number 

Counting in 2s

1. 22, 24, 26, 28, 30, 32
2. 34, 36, 38, 40, 42, 44
3. 46, 48, 50, 52, 54, 56
4. 12, 14, 16, 18, 20, 22
5. 52, 50, 48, 46, 44, 42
6. 10, 8, 6, 4, 2, 0
7. 40, 42, 44, 46, 48, 50
8. 76, 78, 80, 82, 84, 86
9. 84, 82, 80, 78, 76, 74

12 24 32 36 38 40 50 58 68 74

---

page 4

Properties of number N21

Counting in 5s and 10s

1. 75 **2.** 100 **3.** 40 **4.** 25 **5.** 65 **6.** 60
7. 15 **8.** 20 **9.** 30 **10.** 35 **11.** 70 **12.** 80
13. 85 **14.** 10 **15.** 15 **16.** 100 **17.** 45

1. 80 **2.** 100 **3.** 40 **4.** 30 **5.** 70 **6.** 60 **7.** 20 **8.** 20 **9.** 30
10. 40 **11.** 70 **12.** 80 **13.** 90 **14.** 10 **15.** 20 **16.** 100 **17.** 50

31	32	33	34	35	36	37	38	39	40
41	42	43	44	45	46	47	48	49	50
51	52	53	54	55	56	57	58	59	60
61	62	63	64	65	66	67	68	69	70

---

page 5

Properties of number N21

Counting in 3s and 4s

1. £3·50 **2.** £3·50 **3.** £3·00 **4.** £2·50 **5.** £3·00 **6.** £3·00 **7.** £2·50

Any multiple of 12.

Explore

60

Number Textbook 2

page 6

Multiplication/division **N22**

Sixes

1. 4 x 6 = 24 **2.** 6 x 6 = 36 **3.** 8 x 6 = 48 **4.** 3 x 6 = 18
5. 5 x 6 = 30 **6.** 1 x 6 = 6 **7.** 9 x 6 = 54 **8.** 7 x 6 = 42
9. 10 x 6 = 60 **10.** 2 x 6 = 12

11. 4 x 6 = 24 **12.** 3 x 6 = 18 **13.** 5 x 6 = 30 **14.** 2 x 6 = 12
15. 7 x 6 = 42 **16.** 10 x 6 = 60 **17.** 8 x 6 = 48 **18.** 6 x 6 = 36
19. 1 x 6 = 6 **20.** 9 x 6 = 54

e 6 12 18 24 30 36 42 48 54 60 66 72

---

page 7

Multiplication/division **N22**

Sixes

1. 36 ÷ 6 = 6 **2.** 12 ÷ 6 = 2 **3.** 60 ÷ 6 = 10 **4.** 24 ÷ 6 = 4
5. 30 ÷ 6 = 5 **6.** 18 ÷ 6 = 3 **7.** 42 ÷ 6 = 7 **8.** 48 ÷ 6 = 8
9. 66 ÷ 6 = 11 **10.** 54 ÷ 6 = 9

e **1.** 12 **2.** 4 **3.** 20 **4.** 8 **5.** 10 **6.** 6 **7.** 14 **8.** 16 **9.** 22 **10.** 18

11. 3 x 6 = 18 **12.** 7 x 6 = 42 **13.** 60 ÷ 6 = 10 **14.** 5 x 6 = 30
15. 18 ÷ 6 = 3 **16.** 6 ÷ 6 = 1 **17.** 36 ÷ 6 = 6 **18.** 9 x 6 = 54
19. 30 ÷ 6 = 5 **20.** 54 ÷ 6 = 9 **21.** 6 x 6 = 36 **22.** 24 ÷ 6 = 4
23. 7 x 6 = 42

---

page 8

Multiplication/division **N22**

Sixes

1. 2 x 3p = 6p 3 x 6p = 18p 6p + 18p = 24p
2. 3 x 3p = 9p 4 x 6p = 24p 9p + 24p = 33p
3. 5 x 3p = 15p 6 x 6p = 36p 15p + 36p = 51p
4. 1 x 3p = 3p 4 x 6p = 24p 3p + 24p = 27p
5. 2 x 3p = 6p 8 x 6p = 48p 6p + 48p = 54p
6. 9 x 6p = 54p
7. 4 x 3p = 12p 5 x 6p = 30p 12p + 30p = 42p
8. 6 x 3p = 18p 4 x 6p = 24p 18p + 24p = 42p

e 30p, 33p, 36p, 39p, 42p, 45p, 48p, 51p, 54p, 57p, 60p

Explore

Answers are all multiples of 3.

Number Textbook 2

page 9

Multiplication/division **N23**

Nines

1. 1 x 9 = 9
2. 2 x 9 = 18
3. 3 x 9 = 27
4. 4 x 9 = 36
5. 5 x 9 = 45
6. 6 x 9 = 54
7. 7 x 9 = 63
8. 8 x 9 = 72
9. 9 x 9 = 81
10. 10 x 9 = 90

11. 4 x 9 = 36
12. 6 x 9 = 54
13. 5 x 9 = 45
14. 1 x 9 = 9
15. 3 x 9 = 27
16. 8 x 9 = 72
17. 9 x 9 = 81
18. 7 x 9 = 63
19. 2 x 9 = 18

---

page 10

Multiplication/division **N23**

Nines

1. 45 ÷ 9 = 5
2. 27 ÷ 9 = 3
3. 9 ÷ 9 = 1
4. 90 ÷ 9 = 10
5. 63 ÷ 9 = 7
6. 18 ÷ 9 = 2
7. 54 ÷ 9 = 6
8. 36 ÷ 9 = 4
9. 72 ÷ 9 = 8
10. 81 ÷ 9 = 9

11. 2 x 9 = 18
12. 5 x 9 = 45
13. 4 x 9 = 36
14. 9 x 9 = 81
15. 7 x 9 = 63
16. 8 x 9 = 72
17. 10 x 9 = 90
18. 3 x 9 = 27
19. 6 x 9 = 54

Explore

18 27 36 45 90 or 81 72 63 54 90

---

page 11

Nines

	x 9 table		adding the digits	
1.	2 x 9 =	18	1 + 8 =	9
2.	3 x 9 =	27	2 + 7 =	9
3.	4 x 9 =	36	3 + 6 =	9
4.	5 x 9 =	45	4 + 5 =	9
5.	6 x 9 =	54	5 + 4 =	9
6.	7 x 9 =	63	6 + 3 =	9
7.	8 x 9 =	72	7 + 2 =	9
8.	9 x 9 =	81	8 + 1 =	9
9.	10 x 9 =	90	9 + 0 =	9

Number Textbook 2

page 11 cont ...

Multiplication/division **N23**

1. 7 **2.** 5 **3.** 3 **4.** 1 **5.** 1 **6.** 3 **7.** 5 **8.** 7 **9.** 9
The differences are all consecutive odd numbers.

10. 5 x 9 = 45 6 x 9 = 54 **11.** 4 x 9 = 36 7 x 9 = 63
12. 3 x 9 = 27 8 x 9 = 72 **13.** 2 x 9 = 18 9 x 9 = 81
14. 1 x 9 = 9 10 x 9 = 90

---

page 12

Multiplication/division **N24**

Sevens

1. 4 x 7 = 28 days **2.** 2 x 7 = 14 days **3.** 1 x 7 = 7 days
4. 6 x 7 = 42 days **5.** 8 x 7 = 56 days **6.** 7 x 7 = 49 days
7. 9 x 7 = 63 days **8.** 5 x 7 = 35 days **9.** 11 x 7 = 77 days
10. 10 x 7 = 70 days **11.** 3 x 7 = 21 days **12.** 12 x 7 = 84 days
13. 13 x 7 = 91 days

14. 4 x 7 = 28 **15.** 5 x 7 = 35 **16.** 2 x 7 = 14 **17.** 10 x 7 = 70
18. 3 x 7 = 21 **19.** 6 x 7 = 42 **20.** 11 x 7 = 77 **21.** 8 x 7 = 56
22. 7 x 7 = 49 **23.** 9 x 7 = 63

---

page 13

Multiplication/division 

Sevens

1. 14 ÷ 7 = 2 weeks **2.** 28 ÷ 7 = 4 weeks **3.** 42 ÷ 7 = 6 weeks
4. 49 ÷ 7 = 7 weeks **5.** 63 ÷ 7 = 9 weeks **6.** 35 ÷ 7 = 5 weeks
7. 21 ÷ 7 = 3 weeks **8.** 70 ÷ 7 = 10 weeks **9.** 56 ÷ 7 = 8 weeks

Answers will vary.

10. 42 ÷ 7 = 6 **11.** 14 ÷ 7 = 2 **12.** 28 ÷ 7 = 4 **13.** 70 ÷ 7 = 10
14. 21 ÷ 7 = 3 **15.** 7 ÷ 7 = 1 **16.** 35 ÷ 7 = 5 **17.** 56 ÷ 7 = 8
18. 49 ÷ 7 = 7 **19.** 63 ÷ 7 = 9

10. 6 x 7 = 42 **11.** 2 x 7 = 14 **12.** 4 x 7 = 28 **13.** 10 x 7 = 70
14. 3 x 7 = 21 **15.** 1 x 7 = 7 **16.** 5 x 7 = 35 **17.** 8 x 7 = 56
18. 7 x 7 = 49 **19.** 9 x 7 = 63

Number Textbook 2

page 14

Sevens

1	2	3	4	5	6	7	8	9	10
2	4	6	8	10	12	14	16	18	20
3	6	9	12	15	18	21	24	27	30
4	8	12	16	20	24	28	32	36	40
5	10	15	20	25	30	35	40	45	50
6	12	18	24	30	36	42	48	54	60
7	14	21	28	35	42	49	56	63	70
8	16	24	32	40	48	56	64	72	80
9	18	27	36	45	54	63	72	81	90
10	20	30	40	50	60	70	80	90	100

Numbers that appear most on grid: 6, 8, 10, 12, 18, 20, 24, 30, 40 (4 times)
Numbers that appear once only: 1, 25, 49, 64, 81, 100

1. 2 x 7 = 14 **2.** 5 x 7 = 35 **3.** 21 ÷ 7 = 3 **4.** 35 ÷ 7 = 5
5. 42 ÷ 7 = 6 **6.** 9 x 7 = 63 **7.** 7 ÷ 7 = 1 **8.** 8 x 7 = 56
9. 4 x 7 = 28 **10.** 77 ÷ 7 = 11

Explore

7	14	21	28	35	42	49	56	63	70
77	84	91	98	105	112	119	126	133	140

Summing the digits of each number to a single digit:

7	5	3	1	8	6	4	2	9	7
5	3	1	8	6	4	2	9	7	5

Pattern: 7, 5, 3, 1, 8, 6, 4, 2, 9, 7, 5, …

Number Textbook 2

page 15

Multiplication/division N25

Tens and hundreds

1. 13 x 10p = 130p = £1·30
2. 19 x 10p = 190p = £1·90
3. 23 x 10p = 230p = £2·30
4. 10 x 10p = 100p = £1·00
5. 21 x 10p = 210p = £2·10
6. 30 x 10p = 300p = £3·00
7. 22 x 10p = 220p = £2·20
8. 16 x 10p = 160p = £1·60
9. 15 x 10p = 150p = £1·50

10. 35 bananas
11. 1 banana
12. 10 bananas
13. 48 bananas
14. 28 bananas
15. 56 bananas
16. 42 bananas

---

page 16

Multiplication/division N25

Tens and hundreds

1. £1·50
2. £2·00
3. £1·10
4. 60p
5. £4·80
6. £3·60
7. £5·30

e 1. £15 2. £20 3. £11 4. £6 5. £48 6. £36 7. £53

8. 1200 cm
9. 1400 cm
10. 3100 cm
11. 600 cm
12. 5000 cm
13. 3600 cm
14. 2800 cm
15. 1800 cm
16. 6300 cm

---

page 17

Multiplication/division N25

Tens and hundreds

1. 400 ÷ 100 = 4 boxes
2. 300 ÷ 100 = 3 boxes
3. 900 ÷ 100 = 9 boxes
4. 6000 ÷ 100 = 60 boxes
5. 2500 ÷ 100 = 25 boxes
6. 800 ÷ 100 = 8 boxes
7. 7200 ÷ 100 = 72 boxes

8. 70 x 10 = 700
9. 3 x 100 = 300
10. 700 ÷ 10 = 70
11. 1000 ÷ 100 = 10
12. 9000 ÷ 10 = 900
13. 24 x 10 = 240
14. 40 x 100 = 4000
15. 800 ÷ 100 = 8
16. 4000 ÷ 10 = 400

17a. £7·80 = 780p 780 ÷ 10 = 78 78 coins
b. 78 + 15 = 93 coins 93 x 10p = 930p = £9·30 has £9·30 now
c. £9·30 – £3·99 = £5·31 has £5·31 left

Number Textbook 2

page 18

Multiplication/division N26

Multiplying

1. 3 x 30p = 90p
2. 3 x 20p = 60p
3. 3 x 50p = 150p
4. 3 x 40p = 120p
5. 3 x 80p = 240p
6. 3 x 60p = 180p
7. 3 x £1 = £3

1a. 4 x 30p = 120p
2a. 4 x 20p = 80p
3a. 4 x 50p = 200p
4a. 4 x 40p = 160p
5a. 4 x 80p = 320p
6a. 4 x 60p = 240p
7a. 4 x £1 = £4

1b. 2 x 30p = 60p
2b. 2 x 20p = 40p
3b. 2 x 50p = 100p
4b. 2 x 40p = 80p
5b. 2 x 80p = 160p
6b. 2 x 60p = 120p
7b. 2 x £1 = £2

8. 2 x 10p = 20p
9. 2 x 60p = 120p
10. 3 x 30p = 90p
11. 4 x 20p = 80p
12. 3 x 50p = 150p
13. 3 x 40p = 120p
14. 4 x 40p = 160p
15. 4 x 30p = 120p
16. 4 x 60p = 240p

---

page 19

Multiplication/division N26

Multiplying

1. 4 x 22

	20	2
4	80	8

80 + 8 = 88 buns

2. 4 x 24

	20	4
4	80	16

80 + 16 = 96 buns

3. 4 x 32

	30	2
4	120	8

120 + 8 = 128 buns

4. 4 x 15

	10	5
4	40	20

40 + 20 = 60 buns

5. 4 x 26

	20	6
4	80	24

80 + 24 = 104 buns

6. 4 x 19

	10	9
4	40	36

40 + 36 = 76 buns

Number Textbook 2

page 19 cont ...

Multiplication/division N26

7. 4 x 41

	40	1
4	160	4

160 + 4 = 164 buns

8. 4 x 23

	20	3
4	80	12

80 + 12 = 92 buns

9. 4 x 36

	30	6
4	120	24

120 + 24 = 144 buns

10. 4 x 34

	30	4
4	120	16

120 + 16 = 136 buns

11. 4 x 11

	10	1
4	40	4

40 + 4 = 44 buns

12. 2 x 21 = 40 + 2 = 42
13. 3 x 24 = 60 + 12 = 72
14. 4 x 31 = 120 + 4 = 124
15. 5 x 26 = 100 + 30 = 130
16. 4 x 24 = 80 + 16 = 96
17. 6 x 23 = 120 + 18 = 138
18. 2 x 43 = 80 + 6 = 86
19. 3 x 22 = 60 + 6 = 66
20. 5 x 33 = 150 + 15 = 165
21. 7 x 24 = 140 + 28 = 168
22. 8 x 42 = 320 + 16 = 336
23. 5 x 51 = 250 + 5 = 255
24. 9 x 15 = 90 + 45 = 135
25. 6 x 36 = 180 + 36 = 216
26. 3 x 34 = 90 + 12 = 102
27. 4 x 35 = 120 + 20 = 140
28. 2 x 32 = 60 + 4 = 64

---

page 20

Multiplication/division 

Multiplying

1. 2 x 42p = 84p
2. 8 x 24p = 192p = £1·92
3. 5 x 53p = 265p = £2·65
4. 4 x 31p = 124p = £1·24
5. 3 x 62p = 186p = £1·86
6. 9 x 13p = 117p = £1·17
7. 4 x 53p = 212p = £2·12
8. 5 x 24p = 120p = £1·20
9. 7 x 62p = 434p = £4·34
10. 4 x 42p = 168p = £1·68
11. 3 x 13p = 39p
12. 7 x 31p = 217p = £2·17
13. 9 x 24p = 216p = £2·16

Explore

2 x 60 = 120, 3 x 40 = 120, 4 x 30 = 120, 5 x 24 = 120, 6 x 20 = 120, 8 x 15 = 120
2 x 72 = 144, 3 x 48 = 144, 4 x 36 = 144, 6 x 24 = 144, 8 x 18 = 144, 9 x 16 = 144

Number Textbook 2

page 21

Fractions/decimals **N27**

Fractions

1. $\frac{3}{4}$ 2. $\frac{5}{6}$ 3. $\frac{3}{8}$ 4. $\frac{3}{5}$ 5. $\frac{5}{9}$ 6. $\frac{7}{10}$

7. $\frac{1}{8}$ 8. $\frac{1}{6}$ 9. $\frac{1}{10}$ 10. $\frac{1}{8}$ 11. $\frac{1}{2}$ 12. $\frac{2}{5}$

13. $\frac{3}{4}$ 14. $\frac{9}{10}$ 15. $\frac{4}{6}$ 16. $\frac{7}{9}$ 17. $\frac{3}{4}$ 18. $\frac{5}{8}$

e $\frac{1}{10}, \frac{1}{9}, \frac{1}{8}, \frac{1}{6}, \frac{1}{4}, \frac{3}{8}, \frac{2}{5}, \frac{1}{2}, \frac{5}{9}, \frac{3}{5} = \frac{6}{10}, \frac{5}{8}, \frac{4}{6}, \frac{7}{10}, \frac{3}{4}, \frac{7}{9}, \frac{4}{5}, \frac{5}{6}, \frac{9}{10}$

---

page 22

Fractions/decimals **N27**

Fractions

1. $\frac{3}{8}$ 2. $\frac{1}{3}$ 3. $\frac{3}{5}$ 4. $\frac{3}{4}$ 5. $\frac{3}{6}$ 6. $\frac{2}{3}$

7. $\frac{3}{5}$ 8. $\frac{5}{6}$ 9. $\frac{4}{8}$ 10. $\frac{2}{4}$

1a. $\frac{3}{8} < \frac{1}{2}$ 2a. $\frac{1}{3} < \frac{1}{2}$ 3a. $\frac{3}{5} > \frac{1}{2}$ 4a. $\frac{3}{4} > \frac{1}{2}$ 5a. $\frac{3}{6} = \frac{1}{2}$ 6a. $\frac{2}{3} > \frac{1}{2}$

7a. $\frac{3}{5} > \frac{1}{2}$ 8a. $\frac{5}{6} > \frac{1}{2}$ 9a. $\frac{4}{8} = \frac{1}{2}$ 10a. $\frac{2}{4} = \frac{1}{2}$

Explore

Answers will vary.

---

page 23

Fractions/decimals **N27**

Fractions

a $\frac{1}{3}$ b $\frac{2}{3}$ c $\frac{1}{6}$ d $\frac{3}{6} = \frac{1}{2}$ e $\frac{4}{6} = \frac{2}{3}$ f $\frac{1}{4}$

g $\frac{2}{4} = \frac{1}{2}$ h $\frac{3}{4}$ i $\frac{1}{8}$ j $\frac{3}{8}$ k $\frac{5}{8}$ l $\frac{7}{8}$

1. $\frac{1}{3} > \frac{1}{4}$ 2. $\frac{1}{8} < \frac{1}{6}$ 3. $\frac{3}{6} = \frac{2}{4}$ 4. $\frac{3}{4} < \frac{7}{8}$ 5. $\frac{2}{3} = \frac{4}{6}$ 6. $\frac{3}{8} < \frac{2}{4}$

7. $\frac{5}{8} < \frac{4}{6}$ 8. $\frac{2}{3} < \frac{3}{4}$

9. $\frac{1}{3} < \frac{2}{3}$ 10. $\frac{3}{4} > \frac{1}{4}$ 11. $\frac{1}{5} < \frac{1}{2}$ 12. $\frac{1}{2} < \frac{3}{4}$ 13. $\frac{2}{3} > \frac{1}{5}$ 14. $\frac{4}{8} = \frac{2}{4}$

15. $\frac{7}{10} > \frac{2}{5}$ 16. $\frac{3}{6} = \frac{1}{2}$ 17. $\frac{4}{5} > \frac{3}{4}$

e Answers will vary.

Number Textbook 2

page 24

Fractions/decimals **N28**

Fractions

1. $\frac{1}{4}$ of 12p = 3p
2. $\frac{2}{4}$ of 12p = 6p
3. $\frac{3}{4}$ of 12p = 9p
4. $\frac{4}{4}$ of 12p =12p
5. $\frac{1}{3}$ of 15p = 5p
6. $\frac{2}{3}$ of 15p = 10p
7. $\frac{3}{3}$ of 15p = 15p
8. $\frac{1}{5}$ of 20p = 4p
9. $\frac{2}{5}$ of 20p = 8p
10. $\frac{3}{5}$ of 20p = 12p
11. $\frac{4}{5}$ of 20p = 16p
12. $\frac{5}{5}$ of 20p = 20p

● Answers will vary.

Explore

Answers will vary.

---

page 25

Fractions/decimals **N28**

Fractions

1. $\frac{1}{4}$ of 8 = 2
2. $\frac{1}{3}$ of 6 = 2
3. $\frac{3}{8}$ of 8 = 3
4. $\frac{3}{4}$ of 8 = 6
5. $\frac{2}{5}$ of 10 = 4
6. $\frac{2}{3}$ of 9 = 6
7. $\frac{2}{3}$ of 6 = 4
8. $\frac{5}{6}$ of 12 = 10
9. $\frac{1}{4}$ of 12 = 3
10. $\frac{4}{5}$ of 10 = 8

● **1.** $\frac{1}{2}$ **2.** $\frac{1}{6}$ **3.** $\frac{1}{4}$ **4.** $\frac{5}{8}$ **5.** $\frac{3}{5}$ **6.** $\frac{1}{3}$ **7.** $\frac{1}{3}$ **8.** $\frac{1}{3}$ **9.** $\frac{1}{2}$ **10.** $\frac{7}{10}$

11. $\frac{1}{3}$ of 9 = 3
12. $\frac{1}{4}$ of 8 = 2
13. $\frac{2}{4}$ of 8 = 4
14. $\frac{3}{4}$ of 8 = 6
15. $\frac{1}{3}$ of 6 = 2
16. $\frac{2}{3}$ of 6 = 4
17. $\frac{3}{3}$ of 6 = 6
18. $\frac{1}{2}$ of 12 = 6
19. $\frac{2}{4}$ of 12 = 6

---

page 26

Fractions/decimals **N28**

Fractions

1. $\frac{2}{3}$ of 12 = 8
2. $\frac{5}{6}$ of 18 = 15
3. $\frac{1}{6}$ of 12 = 2
4. $\frac{2}{4}$ of 12 = 6
5. $\frac{4}{5}$ of 10 = 8
6. $\frac{2}{3}$ of 9 = 6
7. $\frac{1}{3}$ of 15 = 5
8. $\frac{1}{4}$ of 16 = 4

● **1.** $\frac{1}{3}$ of 12 = 4 **2.** $\frac{1}{6}$ of 18 = 3 **3.** $\frac{5}{6}$ of 12 = 10 **4.** $\frac{2}{4}$ of 12 = 6
5. $\frac{1}{5}$ of 10 = 2 **6.** $\frac{1}{3}$ of 9 = 3 **7.** $\frac{2}{3}$ of 15 = 10 **8.** $\frac{3}{4}$ of 16 = 12

9. $\frac{3}{5}$ of barrel = 24 apples $\frac{1}{5}$ = 8 apples 8 x 5 = 40 40 apples in total

10. $\frac{1}{2}$ of £24 = £12 $\frac{1}{4}$ of £24 = £6 $\frac{1}{6}$ of £24 = £4

£12 + £6 + £4 = £22 £24 – £22 = £2 he has £2 left

Number Textbook 2

page 27

Place-value N29

Rounding

1. 366 → g　2. 374 → d　3. 367 → b　4. 379 → e
5. 371 → h　6. 361 → a　7. 370 → c　8. 378 → j
9. 375 → i　10. 364 → f

1a. 366 → 370　2a. 374 → 370　3a. 367 → 370　4a. 379 → 380
5a. 371 → 370　6a. 361 → 360　7a. 370 → 370　8a. 378 → 380
9a. 375 → 380　10a. 364 → 360

a 330 cm → 300 cm　b 360 cm → 400 cm
c 390 cm → 400 cm　d 620 cm → 600 cm
e 650 cm → 700 cm　f 690 cm → 700 cm
g 810 cm → 800 cm　h 840 cm → 800 cm
i 870 cm → 900 cm

---

page 28

Place-value N29

Rounding

1. 258 g　2. 316 g　3. 211 g　4. 273 g　5. 385 g　6. 284 g
7. 357 g　8. 249 g　9. 332 g

1a. 258 g → 260 g　258 g → 300 g　2a. 316 g → 320 g　316 g → 300 g
3a. 211 g → 210 g　211 g → 200 g　4a. 273 g → 270 g　273 g → 300 g
5a. 385 g → 390 g　385 g → 400 g　6a. 284 g → 280 g　284 g → 300 g
7a. 357 g → 360 g　357 g → 400 g　8a. 249 g → 250 g　249 g → 200 g
9a. 332 g → 330 g　332 g → 300 g

Explore

427 → 430　427 → 400　472 → 470　472 → 500
724 → 720　724 → 700　742 → 740　742 → 700
247 → 250　247 → 200　274 → 270　274 → 300

Five nearest hundreds.

---

page 29

Place-value N29

Rounding

1. 346p　2. 248p　3. 125p　4. 461p　5. 314p　6. 640p
7. 307p　8. 218p　9. 511p　10. 606p

page 29 cont ...

Place-value N29

1a. 346p → 350p 346p → 300p → £3
2a. 248p → 250p 248p → 200p → £2
3a. 125p → 130p 125p → 100p → £1
4a. 461p → 460p 461p → 500p → £5
5a. 314p → 310p 314p → 300p → £3
6a. 640p → 640p 640p → 600p → £6
7a. 307p → 310p 307p → 300p → £3
8a. 218p → 220p 218p → 200p → £2
9a. 511p → 510p 511p → 500p → £5
10a. 606p → 610p 606p → 600p → £6

Explore

Numbers with 460 as the nearest ten: 455, 456, 457, 458, 459, 460, 461, 462, 463, 464

One hundred answers altogether. Answers will vary.

---

page 30

Addition/subtraction N30

Adding two numbers

1. 226 + 180 = 406 **2.** 416 + 375 = 791 **3.** 175 + 236 = 411
4. 244 + 367 = 611 **5.** 364 + 138 = 502 **6.** 333 + 579 = 912
7. 565 + 236 = 801 **8.** 109 + 463 = 572 **9.** 277 + 524 = 801

10. 283 + 158 = 441 m **11.** 294 + 158 = 452 m **12.** 178 + 158 = 336 m
13. 227 + 158 = 385 m **14.** 199 + 158 = 357 m **15.** 285 + 158 = 443 m
16. 207 + 158 = 365 m

---

page 31

Addition/subtraction N30

Adding 3-digit numbers

1. 255 g + 375 g = 630 g **2.** 341 g + 489 g = 830 g
3. 248 g + 367 g = 615 g **4.** 371 g + 299 g = 670 g
5. 176 g + 265 g = 441 g **6.** 353 g + 448 g = 801 g
7. 527 g + 366 g = 893 g **8.** 234 g + 259 g = 493 g
9. 619 g + 191 g = 810 g **10.** 355 g + 455 g = 810 g

402 + 98 = 500 226 + 274 = 500 236 + 264 = 500 178 + 322 = 500
244 + 256 = 500 358 + 142 = 500

Number Textbook 2

page 32

Addition/subtraction N30

Adding 3-digit numbers

1. 96 + 124 + 78 + 168 = 466 runs
2. 87 + 225 + 184 + 96 = 592 runs
3. 123 + 214 + 119 + 267 = 723 runs
4. 75 + 242 + 98 + 108 = 523 runs
5. 256 + 125 + 118 + 87 = 586 runs
6. 144 + 241 + 109 + 218 = 712 runs

Explore

Answers will vary.
Highest possible score is 3, by making 1000.

---

page 33

Addition/subtraction N31

Subtracting multiples of 10

1. 367 – 80 = 287
2. 256 – 80 = 176
3. 373 – 80 = 293
4. 552 – 80 = 472
5. 147 – 80 = 67
6. 608 – 80 = 528
7. 431 – 80 = 351
8. 824 – 80 = 744
9. 912 – 80 = 832

e 287 – 50 = 237
176 – 50 = 126
293 – 50 = 243
472 – 50 = 422
67 – 50 = 17
528 – 50 = 478
351 – 50 = 301
744 – 50 = 694
832 – 50 = 782

10. 374 – 80 = 294
11. 254 – 70 = 184
12. 171 – 90 = 81
13. 554 – 60 = 494
14. 333 – 60 = 273
15. 742 – 80 = 662
16. 681 – 90 = 591
17. 625 – 70 = 555
18. 423 – 50 = 373
19. 217 – 40 = 177
20. 892 – 70 = 822
21. 711 – 60 = 651

---

page 34

Addition/subtraction N31

Subtracting multiples of 10

1. 116 – 30 = 86 minutes
2. 121 – 40 = 81 minutes
3. 119 – 50 = 69 minutes
4. 127 – 60 = 67 minutes
5. 142 – 90 = 52 minutes
6. 123 – 70 = 53 minutes
7. 122 – 30 = 92 minutes
8. 132 – 50 = 82 minutes
9. 118 – 60 = 58 minutes

243 – 60 = 183
243 – 70 = 173
243 – 80 = 163

332 – 60 = 272
332 – 70 = 262
332 – 80 = 252

418 – 60 = 358
418 – 70 = 348
418 – 80 = 338

Number Textbook 2

page 35

Addition/subtraction 

Subtracting multiples of 10

–	241	321	106	445	211
30	211	291	76	415	181
60	181	261	46	385	151
80	161	241	26	365	131
20	221	301	86	425	191

1. £123 – £60 = £63 £63 left
2. 107 – 70 = 37 37 years old
   107 – 30 = 77 77 years old
3. 500 – 90 = 410 410 pieces
   410 – 80 = 330 330 pieces to do
4. 578 – 80 = 498 498 people left
   498 – 50 = 448 448 people left

---

page 36

Addition/subtraction 

Subtracting

1. 123 – 56 = 67
2. 173 – 88 = 85
3. 142 – 65 = 77
4. 214 – 178 = 36
5. 123 – 76 = 47
6. 122 – 67 = 55
7. 204 – 166 = 38
8. 214 – 155 = 59
9. 184 – 95 = 89
10. 133 – 74 = 59
11. 311 – 294 = 17
12. 177 – 67 = 110
13. 405 – 328 = 77
14. 338 – 282 = 56

15. 121 – 38 = 83 minutes
16. 126 – 38 = 88 minutes
17. 132 – 38 = 94 minutes
18. 144 – 38 = 106 minutes
19. 137 – 38 = 99 minutes
20. 118 – 38 = 80 minutes

---

page 37

Addition/subtraction N32

Subtracting

1. 114 – 65 = 49
2. 186 – 71 = 115
3. 223 – 126 = 97
4. 119 – 47 = 72
5. 253 – 198 = 55
6. 207 – 114 = 93
7. 245 – 133 = 112
8. 118 – 53 = 65
9. 302 – 213 = 89

10. 243 – 167 = 76
11. 314 – 268 = 46
12. 417 – 347 = 70
13. 624 – 586 = 38
14. 709 – 644 = 65
15. 313 – 277 = 36
16. 424 – 386 = 38
17. 503 – 479 = 24
18. 257 – 134 = 123
19. 303 – 223 = 80

Number Textbook 2

page 38

Addition/subtraction N32

Subtracting

1. 343 – 157 = 186 miles
2. 241 – 173 = 68 miles
3. 411 – 274 = 137 miles
4. 236 – 91 = 145 miles
5. 454 – 232 = 222 miles
6. 318 – 107 = 211 miles
7. 413 – 102 = 311 miles

1. 343 + 157 = 500 miles
2. 241 + 173 = 414 miles
3. 411 + 274 = 685 miles
4. 236 + 91 = 327 miles
5. 454 + 232 = 686 miles
6. 318 + 107 = 425 miles
7. 413 + 102 = 515 miles

Explore

Answers will vary.

Smallest possible difference: 723 – 684 = 39 or 426 – 387 = 39

Largest possible difference: 876 – 234 = 642

Nearest difference to 400: 862 – 473 = 398

---

page 39

Addition/subtraction 

Subtracting

1. 346 – 129 = 217
2. 537 – 162 = 375
3. 341 – 225 = 116
4. 463 – 245 = 218
5. 471 – 322 = 149
6. 564 – 127 = 437
7. 562 – 226 = 336
8. 672 – 348 = 324
9. 372 – 148 = 224
10. 273 – 129 = 144
11. 614 – 372 = 242
12. 727 – 366 = 361
13. 912 – 431 = 481
14. 504 – 271 = 233
15. 456 – 271 = 185
16. 332 – 170 = 162
17. 406 – 282 = 124

814 – 459 = 355	814 – 367 = 447	814 – 188 = 626
943 – 459 = 484	943 – 367 = 576	943 – 188 = 755
721 – 459 = 262	721 – 367 = 354	721 – 188 = 533

---

page 40

Addition/subtraction N33

Subtracting

1. 336 – 183 = 153
2. 528 – 262 = 266
3. 328 – 191 = 137
4. 337 – 148 = 189
5. 347 – 158 = 189
6. 364 – 192 = 172
7. 329 – 155 = 174
8. 337 – 165 = 172
9. 403 – 181 = 222
10. 327 – 164 = 163

Number Textbook 2

page 40 cont ...

Addition/subtraction N33

1a. 183 – 153 = 30 2a. 266 – 262 = 4 3a. 191 – 137 = 54
4a. 189 – 148 = 41 5a. 189 – 158 = 31 6a. 192 – 172 = 20
7a. 174 – 155 = 19 8a. 172 – 165 = 7 9a. 222 – 181 = 41
10a. 164 – 163 = 1

---

page 41

Addition/subtraction N33

Subtracting

1. 472 – 216 = 256 g 2. 224 – 157 = 67 g 3. 336 – 172 = 164 g
4. 417 – 208 = 209 g 5. 293 – 144 = 149 g 6. 515 – 273 = 242 g
7. 483 – 197 = 286 g 8. 377 – 159 = 218 g 9. 333 – 177 = 156 g

10. 237 – 128 = 109 109 boys
11. 365 – 176 = 189 189 days

---

page 42

Properties of number N34

Odd and even

1. 472	even	2. 555	odd	3. 641	odd
4. 229	odd	5. 318	even	6. 744	even
7. 908	even	8. 163	odd	9. 227	odd
10. 842	even	11. 669	odd	12. 343	odd
13. 516	even	14. 732	even		

15. 78, 80, 82 16. 116, 118, 120 17. 310, 312, 314
18. 968, 970, 972 19. 196, 198, 200 20. 438, 440, 442
21. 514, 516, 518 22. 666, 668, 670 23. 798, 800, 802
24. 444, 446, 448 25. 396, 398, 400 26. 108, 110, 112
27. 998, 1000, 1002

e

15. 74, 76 16. 112, 114 17. 306, 308 18. 964, 966
19. 192, 194 20. 434, 436 21. 510, 512 22. 662, 664
23. 794, 796 24. 440, 442 25. 392, 394 26. 104, 106
27. 994, 996

Number Textbook 2

page 43

Odd and even

+	1	2	3	4	5	6
1	2	3	4	5	6	7
2	3	4	5	6	7	8
3	4	5	6	7	8	9
4	5	6	7	8	9	10
5	6	7	8	9	10	11
6	7	8	9	10	11	12

= blue

= yellow

= red

odd + odd = even
even + even = even
odd + even = even + odd = odd

1. 7 + 9 even
2. 5 + 6 odd
3. 23 + 37 even
4. 42 + 54 even
5. 16 + 12 even
6. 54 + 17 odd
7. 513 + 123 even
8. 138 + 223 odd
9. 565 + 363 even

Explore

Pairs with even totals: 7, 5 2, 4 7, 9 1, 5 3, 7 2, 8 1, 7 9, 5 (8 pairs)
Pairs with odd totals: 3, 8 8, 1 2, 7 4, 9 9, 6 3, 2 8, 7 5, 6 4, 7 8, 5 7, 6 2, 9 (12 pairs)

Number Textbook 2

page 44

Properties of number **N34**

Odd and even

–	7	8	9	10	11	12
1	6	7	8	9	10	11
2	5	6	7	8	9	10
3	4	5	6	7	8	9
4	3	4	5	6	7	8
5	2	3	4	5	6	7
6	1	2	3	4	5	6

= blue

= yellow

= red

odd – odd = even
even – even = even
odd – even = even – odd = odd

1. 15 – 9 = 6
24 – 12 = 12
8 – 7 = 1
Bob's winnings £1 + £1 + 50p = £2·50

2. 12 – 8 = 4
13 – 7 = 6
18 – 9 = 9
Sanjit's winnings £1 + £1 + 50p = £2·50

3. 9 – 3 = 6
21 – 14 = 7
11 – 6 = 5
Jenna's winnings £1 + 50p + 50p = £2

4. 11 – 2 = 9
17 – 9 = 8
24 – 6 = 18
Tim's winnings £1 + £1 + 50p = £2·50

5. 18 – 12 = 6
16 – 9 = 7
22 – 18 = 4
Jo's winnings £1 + £1 + 50p = £2·50

---

page 45

Properties of number **N35**

Negative numbers

1. ¯4 °C **2.** ¯2°C **3.** ¯3 °C **4.** ¯7 °C **5.** ¯1 °C
6. ¯6 °C **7.** ¯8 °C

1. ¯2 °C **2.** 0 °C **3.** ¯1 °C **4.** ¯5 °C **5.** 1 °C **6.** ¯4 °C **7.** ¯6 °C

8. ¯6 °C **9.** ¯9 °C **10.** ¯4 °C **11.** ¯2 °C **12.** ¯7 °C
13. ¯10 °C **14.** ¯12 °C **15.** ¯3 °C

Number Textbook 2

page 46

Properties of number **N35**

Negative numbers

a. $18 - 8 = 10$ **b.** $14 - 8 = 6$ **c.** $8 - 8 = 0$
d. $4 - 8 = {}^{-}4$ **e.** $1 - 8 = {}^{-}7$ **f.** ${}^{-}2 - 8 = {}^{-}10$
g. ${}^{-}5 - 8 = {}^{-}13$ **h.** ${}^{-}9 - 8 = {}^{-}17$ **i.** ${}^{-}12 - 8 = {}^{-}20$
j. ${}^{-}16 - 8 = {}^{-}24$

a. 14 **b.** 10 **c.** 4 **d.** 0 **e.** ${}^{-}3$ **f.** ${}^{-}6$ **g.** ${}^{-}9$ **h.** ${}^{-}13$ **i.** ${}^{-}16$ **j.** ${}^{-}20$

1. ${}^{-}18$ °C → ${}^{-}14$ °C **2.** ${}^{-}14$ °C → ${}^{-}17$ °C **3.** ${}^{-}17$ °C → ${}^{-}12$ °C
4. ${}^{-}12$ °C → ${}^{-}10$ °C **5.** ${}^{-}10$ °C → ${}^{-}18$ °C **6.** ${}^{-}18$ °C → ${}^{-}12$ °C
7. ${}^{-}12$ °C → ${}^{-}5$ °C **8.** ${}^{-}5$ °C → ${}^{-}18$ °C

---

page 47

Properties of number **N35**

Negative numbers

1. Sam still owes 5p. **2.** Lily still owes 3p. **3.** Chuy still owes 10p.
4. Bill still owes 5p. **5.** Simone still owes 6p. **6.** Jon still owes 9p.
7. Hatti still owes 4p. **8.** Samira still owes 6p. **9.** Dan still owes 18p.
10. Amrita still owes 5p. **11.** Jack still owes 11p. **12.** Mel still owes 11p.
13. Vikram still owes 18p.

Explore

$5 + {}^{-}6 = {}^{-}1$ $4 + {}^{-}5 = {}^{-}1$ $3 + {}^{-}4 = {}^{-}1$ $2 + {}^{-}3 = {}^{-}1$ $1 + {}^{-}2 = {}^{-}1$ 5 pairs

---

page 48

Multiplication/division **N36**

Doubling

1. double 360 = 600 + 120 = 720 g **2.** double 240 = 400 + 80 = 480 g
3. double 310 = 600 + 20 = 620 g **4.** double 170 = 200 + 140 = 340 g
5. double 380 = 600 + 160 = 760 g **6.** double 460 = 800 + 120 = 920 g
7. double 190 = 200 + 180 = 380 g

8. double 240 = 400 + 80 = 480 **9.** double 330 = 600 + 60 = 660
10. double 260 = 400 + 120 = 520 **11.** double 470 = 800 + 140 = 940
12. double 180 = 200 + 160 = 360 **13.** double 250 = 400 + 100 = 500
14. double 390 = 600 + 180 = 780

Number Textbook 2

page 49

Multiplication/division **N36**

Halving

1. half of 780 m = 350 + 40 = 390 m
2. half of 540 m = 250 + 20 = 270 m
3. half of 460 m = 200 + 30 = 230 m
4. half of 830 m = 400 + 15 = 415 m
5. half of 920 m = 450 + 10 = 460 m
6. half of 340 m = 150 + 20 = 170 m
7. half of 590 m = 250 + 45 = 295 m

8. half of £580 = 250 + 40 = £290
9. half of £760 = 350 + 30 = £380
10. half of £440 = 200 + 20 = £220
11. half of £320 = 150 + 10 = £160
12. half of £650 = 300 + 25 = £325
13. half of £940 = 450 + 20 = £470
14. half of £380 = 150 + 40 = £190

---

page 50

Multiplication/division **N36**

Doubling and halving

1. 6800 potatoes 9200 carrots 3600 onions 5400 tomatoes
   4200 celery sticks 880 pints of stock
2. 1700 potatoes 2300 carrots 900 onions 1350 tomatoes
   1050 celery sticks 220 pints of stock
3. 850 potatoes 1150 carrots 450 onions 675 tomatoes
   525 celery sticks 110 pints of stock

double

in	out
2300	4600
4500	9000
1700	3400
480	960
3700	7400
290	580
3100	6200

halve

in	out
6800	3400
780	390
4900	2450
2700	1350
8600	4300
930	465
5800	2900

---

page 51

Multiplication/division **N37**

Multiplying

1. 22 x 4 = 88
2. 12 x 3 = 36
3. 32 x 2 = 64
4. 15 x 3 = 45
5. 14 x 5 = 70
6. 35 x 2 = 70
7. 38 x 4 = 152
8. 56 x 2 = 112
9. 29 x 3 = 87
10. 45 x 7 = 315

page 51 cont ...

Multiplication/division N37

11. 27 x 5 = 135 **12.** 15 x 4 = 60 **13.** 21 x 5 = 105 **14.** 32 x 5 = 160
15. 51 x 4 = 204 **16.** 28 x 5 = 140 **17.** 43 x 6 = 258 **18.** 37 x 4 = 148
19. 35 x 7 = 245 **20.** 62 x 5 = 310

---

page 52

Multiplication/division N37

Multiplying

1. 31p x 5 = 155p = £1·55
2. 26p x 4 = 104p = £1·04
3. 18p x 5 = 90p
4. 42p x 6 = 252p = £2·52
5. 26p x 7 = 182p = £1·82
6. 31p x 8 = 248p = £2·48
7. 14p x 7 = 98p

8. 32p x 6 = 192p = £1·92
9. 13p x 5 = 65p
10. 43p x 4= 172p = £1·72
11. 21p x 6 = 126p = £1·26
12. 13p x 8 = 104p = £1·04
13. 32p x 7 = 224p = £2·24
14. 28p x 4 = 112p = £1·12

---

page 53

Multiplication/division N37

Multiplying

1. 23 x 4 = 92 m **2.** 17 x 6 = 102 m **3.** 14 x 5 = 70 m
4. 22 x 4 = 88 m **5.** 13 x 8 = 104 m **6.** 34 x 4 = 136 m
7. 21 x 6 = 126 m **8.** 49 x 4 = 196 m

e Answers will vary.

Explore

Largest possible answer: 43 x 5 = 215 Smallest possible answer: 34 x 2 = 68
24 different answers

---

page 54

Multiplication/division 

Dividing

1. 32p ÷ 10 = 3p r 2p
2. 44p ÷ 10 = 4p r 4p
3. 69p ÷ 10 = 6p r 9p
4. 71p ÷ 10 = 7p r 1p
5. 83p ÷ 10 = 8p r 3p
6. 104p ÷ 10 = 10p r 4p
7. 67p ÷ 10 = 6p r 7p
8. 70p ÷ 10 = 7p
9. 58p ÷ 10 = 5p r 8p

e Answers will vary.

Number Textbook 2

page 54 cont ...

Multiplication/division N38

10. 46 ÷ 5 = 9 r 1 **11.** 13 ÷ 3 = 4 r 1 **12.** 11 ÷ 2 = 5 r 1
13. 37 ÷ 5 = 7 r 2 **14.** 21 ÷ 2 = 10 r 1 **15.** 16 ÷ 5 = 3 r 1
16. 23 ÷ 3 = 7 r 2 **17.** 28 ÷ 5 = 5 r 3 **18.** 25 ÷ 2 = 12 r 1

---

page 55

Multiplication/division N38

Dividing

1. 22 ÷ 5 = 4 r 2 r = 2 bones **2.** 43 ÷ 5 = 8 r 3 r = 3 bones
3. 31 ÷ 5 = 6 r 1 r = 1 bone **4.** 29 ÷ 5 = 5 r 4 r = 4 bones
5. 17 ÷ 5 = 3 r 2 r = 2 bones **6.** 58 ÷ 5 = 11 r 3 r = 3 bones
7. 42 ÷ 5 = 8 r 2 r = 2 bones **8.** 64 ÷ 5 = 12 r 4 r = 4 bones
9. 75 ÷ 5 = 15 r = 0 bones

10. 42 ÷ 5 = 8 r 2 **11.** 20 ÷ 6 = 3 r 2 **12.** 38 ÷ 9 = 4 r 2
13. 33 ÷ 8 = 4 r 1 **14.** 28 ÷ 3 = 9 r 1 **15.** 49 ÷ 6 = 8 r 1
16. 15 ÷ 4 = 3 r 3 **17.** 43 ÷ 8 = 5 r 3 **18.** 66 ÷ 9 = 7 r 3

---

page 56

Multiplication/division N38

Dividing

1. 42 ÷ 5 = 8 r 2 needed 9 tubes
2. 47 ÷ 5 = 9 r 2 can buy 9 tickets
3. 6 x 7 = 42 42 + 3 = 45 45 cakes
4. 47 ÷ 7 = 6 r 5 5 players not in a team

5. 28 ÷ 3 = 9 r 1 **6.** 28 ÷ 2 = 14 **7.** 28 ÷ 8 = 3 r 4
8. 28 ÷ 9 = 3 r 1 **9.** 28 ÷ 5 = 5 r 3 **10.** 28 ÷ 6 = 4 r 4
12. 28 ÷ 7 = 4

Explore

Numbers that divide into 20 exactly: 1, 2, 4, 5, 10, 20
Numbers that divide into 12 exactly: 1, 2, 3, 4, 6, 12
Numbers that divide into 30 exactly: 1, 2, 3, 5, 6, 10, 15, 30
Numbers that divide into 24 exactly: 1, 2, 3, 4, 6, 8, 12, 24

---

page 57

Multiplication/division 

Dividing

1. $4\overline{)48}$ = 12 groups **2.** $2\overline{)24}$ = 12 groups **3.** $2\overline{)36}$ = 18 groups
4. $3\overline{)39}$ = 13 groups **5.** $4\overline{)64}$ = 16 groups **6.** $3\overline{)69}$ = 23 groups
7. $5\overline{)85}$ = 17 groups **8.** $3\overline{)57}$ = 19 groups **9.** $4\overline{)76}$ = 19 groups

page 57 cont ...

Multiplication/division N39

10. $2\overline{)32} = 16$ **11.** $3\overline{)69} = 23$ **12.** $5\overline{)85} = 17$ **13.** $4\overline{)68} = 17$
14. $2\overline{)48} = 24$ **15.** $6\overline{)78} = 13$ **16.** $6\overline{)96} = 16$ **17.** $7\overline{)91} = 13$
18. $5\overline{)65} = 13$ **19.** $3\overline{)96} = 32$ **20.** $7\overline{)98} = 14$ **21.** $4\overline{)76} = 19$

---

page 58

Multiplication/division N39

Dividing

1. $4\overline{)52} = 13$ torches **2.** $3\overline{)63} = 21$ torches **3.** $6\overline{)78} = 13$ torches
4. $4\overline{)84} = 21$ torches **5.** $3\overline{)72} = 24$ torches **6.** $3\overline{)66} = 22$ torches
7. $4\overline{)84} = 21$ torches **8.** $6\overline{)84} = 14$ torches **9.** $3\overline{)93} = 31$ torches
10. $2\overline{)64} = 32$ torches **11.** $3\overline{)72} = 24$ torches

12. $2\overline{)88} = 44$ **13.** $3\overline{)48} = 16$ **14.** $4\overline{)72} = 18$ **15.** $5\overline{)75} = 15$
16. $2\overline{)74} = 37$ **17.** $3\overline{)87} = 29$ **18.** $4\overline{)64} = 16$ **19.** $3\overline{)75} = 25$
20. $2\overline{)92} = 46$ **21.** $3\overline{)81} = 27$ **22.** $3\overline{)93} = 31$

---

page 59

Multiplication/division N39

Dividing

1. $84 \div 4 = 21$ 21 packs
2. £96 ÷ 3 = £32 £32 each
3. $65 \div 5 = 13$ bought 13 crayons
4. $96 \div 6 = 16$ 16 cm long

5. $6\overline{)73} = 12$ r 1 **6.** $4\overline{)66} = 16$ r 2 **7.** $7\overline{)81} = 11$ r 4
8. $3\overline{)47} = 15$ r 2 **9.** $4\overline{)58} = 14$ r 2

Explore

61

---

page 60

Fractions/decimals N40

Tenths

1. $\frac{3}{10}$ **2.** $\frac{5}{10}$ **3.** $\frac{4}{10}$ **4.** $\frac{2}{10}$ **5.** $\frac{1}{10}$
6. $\frac{8}{10}$ **7.** $\frac{10}{10}$ **8.** $\frac{6}{10}$ **9.** $\frac{9}{10}$ **10.** $\frac{7}{10}$

1a. $\frac{3}{10} = 0{\cdot}3$ **2a.** $\frac{5}{10} = 0{\cdot}5$ **3a.** $\frac{4}{10} = 0{\cdot}4$ **4a.** $\frac{2}{10} = 0{\cdot}2$ **5a.** $\frac{1}{10} = 0{\cdot}1$
6a. $\frac{8}{10} = 0{\cdot}8$ **7a.** $\frac{10}{10} = 1{\cdot}0$ **8a.** $\frac{6}{10} = 0{\cdot}6$ **9a.** $\frac{9}{10} = 0{\cdot}9$ **10a.** $\frac{7}{10} = 0{\cdot}7$

page 60 cont ...

Fractions/decimals N40

a 0·4 m	**b** 0·9 m	**c** 1·2 m	**b** 1·7 m	**e** 2·1 m
f 2·6 m	**g** 3·0 m	**h** 3·6 m	**i** 4·3 m	**j** 4·8 m
k 5·1 m	**l** 5·9 m			

---

page 61

Fractions/decimals N40

Tenths

1. h	**2.** c	**3.** f	**4.** e	**5.** a
6. i	**7.** b	**8.** d	**9.** g	
10. 2·4 kg	**11.** 3·6 kg	**12.** 2·5 kg	**13.** 1·3 kg	**14.** 3·8 kg
15. 4·2 kg	**16.** 0·6 kg			

---

page 62

Fractions/decimals 

Tenths

1·1 kg, 1·3 kg, 1·7kg, 2·6 kg, 2·9 kg, 3·6 kg, 3·9 kg, 4·0 kg, 4·2 kg, 4·7kg, 5·1 kg, 5·3 kg

Explore

6 numbers

2·3 2·5 3·2 3·5 5·2 5·3

---

page 63

Fractions/decimals N41

Hundredths

1. £1·25	**2.** £2·52	**3.** £1·31	**4.** £3·30	**5.** £5·10
6. £0·53	**7.** £0·37	**8.** £0·77	**9.** £1·04	**10.** £6·07

11.	a = 2·12	b = 2·14	c = 2·17	d = 2·19		
12.	a = 3·23	b = 3·26	c = 3·29	d = 3·35	e = 3·39	
13.	a = 8·62	b = 8·65	c = 8·66	d = 8·71	e = 8·74	f = 8·78

---

page 64

Fractions/decimals N41

Hundredths

1. 2·25 m	**2.** 1·32 m	**3.** 1·20 m	**4.** 1·30 m
5. 0·5 m or 0·50 m	**6.** 0·45 m	**7.** 2·56 m	**8.** 3·60 m
9. 4·5 m or 4·50 m	**10.** 1·25 m		

page 64 cont ...

Fractions/decimals **N41**

11. k	**12.** d	**13.** i	**14.** f	**15.** b	**16.** g
17. c	**18.** a	**19.** j	**20.** h	**21.** e	

---

page 65

Fractions/decimals **N41**

Hundredths

1. £3·17	**2.** £5·15	**3.** £1·18	**4.** £3·40	**5.** £5·00
6. £3·05	**7.** £7·00	**8.** £7·81	**9.** £1·91	**10.** £7·01
11. £8·03	**12.** £4·41	**13.** £1·83		
14. £8·80	**15.** £7·01	**16.** £4·97	**17.** £5·09	**18.** £9·79
19. £2·99	**20.** £3·89	**21.** £4·48		

---

page 66

Addition/subtraction **N42**

Subtracting

1. 445 – 257 = 188	**2.** 356 – 288 = 68	**3.** 264 – 159 = 105
4. 437 – 258 = 179	**5.** 548 – 289 = 259	**6.** 185 – 97 = 88
7. 244 – 166 = 78	**8.** 343 – 157 = 186	**9.** 322 – 165 = 157
10. 345 – 177 = 168		
11. 564 – 287 = 277	**12.** 473 – 296 = 177	**13.** 885 – 297 = 588
14. 664 – 488 = 176	**15.** 837 – 478 = 359	

---

page 67

Addition/subtraction 

Subtracting

1. 911 – 281 = 630 km	**2.** 911 – 324 = 587 km	**3.** 911 – 365 = 546 km
4. 911 – 482 = 429 km	**5.** 911 – 543 = 368 km	**6.** 911 – 664 = 247 km
7. 911 – 727 = 184 km	**8.** 911 – 786 = 125 km	**9.** 911 – 875 = 36 km

716 – 345 = 371	716 – 488 = 228	716 – 698 = 18
924 – 345 = 579	924 – 488 = 436	924 – 698 = 226
833 – 345 = 488	833 – 488 = 345	833 – 698 = 135

---

page 68

Addition/subtraction 

Subtracting

1. 242 – 115 = 127 m	**2.** 621 – 136 = 485 m	**3.** 221 – 85 = 136 m
4. 624 – 460 = 164 m		

Number Textbook 2

page 68 cont ...

Addition/subtraction N42

5. 213 – 124 = 89 m
6. 321 – 236 = 85 m
7. 263 – 172 = 91 m
8. 305 – 218 = 87 m

9. 518 – 348 = 170 m
10. 646 – 527 = 119 m
11. 685 – 658 = 27 m
12. 902 – 893 = 9 m

Explore

Answers will vary.

---

page 69

Addition/subtraction N43

Adding and subtracting

1. £5·68 + £4·87 = £10·55
2. £13·58 + £7·77 = £21·35
3. £15·49 + £12·75 = £28·24
4. £9·99 + £11·11 = £21·10
5. £4·75 + £3·86 = £8·61
6. £10·49 + £12·87 = £23·36
7. £9·87 + £13·56 = £23·43
8. £9·19 + £7·77 = £16·96
9. £11·29 + £14·98 = £26·27
10. £8·76 + £12·41 = £21·17

11. £4·11 – £2·22 = £1·89
12. £3·50 – £1·75 = £1·75
13. £6·12 – £4·24 = £1·88
14. £4·20 – £1·80 = £2·40
15. £3·17 – £1·77 = £1·40
16. £2·80 – £1·90 = £0·90

---

page 70

Addition/subtraction N43

Subtracting

1. £3·29 – £1·79 = £1·50
2. £5·59 – £3·89 = £1·70
3. £6·38 – £2·98 = £3·40
4. £4·37 – £1·67 = £2·70
5. £10·16 – £2·96 = £7·20
6. £5·29 – £2·79 = £2·50
7. £8·16 – £1·46 = £6·70
8. £7·57 – £3·87 = £3·70
9. £4·26 – £2·76 = £1·50
10. £6·28 – £3·98 = £2·30

£9·98, £7·99 £6·67, £4·68 £3·73, £1·74 £7·54, £5·55 £5·35, £3·36

Number Textbook 2

page 71

Subtracting

1. £19·99 – £8·78 = £11·21
2. £19·99 – £10·19 = £9·80
3. £19·99 – £11·12 = £8·87
4. £19·99 – £5·50 = £14·49
5. £19.99 – £13·75 = £6·24
6. £19·99 – £13·64 = £6·35
7. £19·99 – £11·79 = £8·20
8. £19·99 – £15·75 = £4·24

Explore

Jane is 12, James is 6.

---

page 72

Mixed problems

1. 346 m + 168 m = 514 m   1000 m – 514 m = 486 m   486 m further
2. 346 g + 425 g + 475 g + 582 g = 1828 g   2 x 1828 g = 3656 g
   total weight now 3656 g

3a. 512 – 468 = 44   Mark scored 44 more
 b. Jinda   468 + 275 = 743
    Mark   512 + 196 = 708
    Jinda wins by 35
 c. Jinda   743 – 500 = 243   final score   243 points
    Mark   708 – 400 = 308   final score   308 points

4a. £12·99 + £13·79 + £11·69 = £38·47   £38·50 – £38·47 = 3p
 b. Cannot buy 4 videos for £45, cheapest option £45·26.

Shape, Data and Measures

page 3

Length M1

Centimetres (cm)

1. 4 cm **2.** 6 cm **3.** 8 cm **4.** 3 cm **5.** 10 cm
6. 7 cm **7.** 5 cm

e 40 mm 60 mm 80 mm 30 mm 100 mm 70 mm 50 mm

8–13. Estimates and answers will vary.

---

page 4

Length M1

Centimetres (cm), metres (m), millimetres (mm)

1. 120 cm **2.** 105 cm **3.** 2 cm **4.** 180 cm
5. 230 cm **6.** 4 cm **7.** 156 cm

8. 1 m 30 cm **9.** 2 m 20 cm **10.** 3 m 50 cm
11. 2 m **12.** 5 cm 4 mm **13.** 6 cm 8 mm
14. 9 cm 7 mm **15.** 6 cm

---

page 5

Length 

Metres (m) and kilometres (km)

1. 2 km 543 m **2.** 3 km 342 m **3.** 2 km 230 m
4. 4 km 100 m **5.** 6 km 12 m **6.** 1 km 111 m
7. 3 km 921 m **8.** 3 km 403 m **9.** 1 km 45 m

e **1.** 1 km 271·5 m **2.** 1 km 671 m **3.** 1 km 115 m **4.** 2 km 50 m
5. 3 km 6 m **6.** 555·5 m **7.** 1 km 960·5 m **8.** 1 km 701·5 m
9. 522·5 m

10. 300 ÷ 5 = 60 60 x 3 = 180 miles
11. 100 ÷ 5 = 20 20 x 3 = 60 miles
12. 1000 ÷ 5 = 200 200 x 3 = 600 miles
13. 650 ÷ 5 = 130 130 x 3 = 390 miles
14. 250 ÷ 5 = 50 50 x 3 = 150 miles
15. 350 ÷ 5 = 70 70 x 3 = 210 miles
16. 10 ÷ 5 = 2 2 x 3 = 6 miles
17. 500 ÷ 5 = 100 100 x 3 = 300 miles
18. 50 ÷ 5 = 10 10 x 3 = 30 miles
19. 90 ÷ 5 = 18 18 x 3 = 54 miles
20. 85 ÷ 5 = 17 17 x 3 = 51 miles

Shape, Data and Measures

page 6

Weight **M2**

Grams (g) and kilograms (kg)

1. 1700 g **2.** 1200 g **3.** 2300 g
4. 3150 g **5.** 1900 g **6.** 4100 g
7. 2500 g

8. 1 kg 500 g **9.** 2 kg 300 g **10.** 1 kg 700 g
11. 3 kg **12.** 4 kg 500 g **13.** 1 kg 50 g
14. 2 kg 505 g **15.** 1 kg 675 g **16.** 1 kg 225 g

---

page 7

Weight **M2**

Grams (g) and kilograms (kg)

1–7. Answers will vary.

8. 2 **9.** 4 **10.** 20 **11.** 40 **12.** 8
13. 10 **14.** 4 **15.** 5 **16.** 80

Explore

Put the 1 kg weight on one side of the balance and each kitten in turn on the other side until it balances. This kitten weighs 1 kg. Next put the three remaining kittens on opposite sides of the balance to find the one that always makes the balance go down. This kitten is the heaviest – 1 kg 300 g. Then put the two remaining kittens on opposite sides of the balance. The heavier one is 1 kg 200 g; the lighter one is 1 kg 100 g.

---

page 8

Weight **M2**

Grams (g) and kilograms (kg)

1–8. Estimates will vary.

1. grams **2.** grams **3.** grams **4.** kilograms
5. kilograms **6.** kilograms **7.** kilograms **8.** grams

9. 4×200 g = 800g   1000 g – 800 g = 200g   200 g left
10. 25 kg – $2\frac{1}{2}$ kg = $22\frac{1}{2}$ kg $22\frac{1}{2}$ kg + $\frac{3}{4}$ kg = $23\frac{1}{4}$ kg

Shape, Data and Measures

page 9

Capacity M3

Millilitres (ml) and litres (l)

1. 1200 ml
2. 1400 ml
3. 400 ml
4. 200 ml
5. 700 ml
6. 300 ml
7. 1000 ml
8. 900 ml
9. 1800 ml

10. 1 l 700 ml
11. 2 l 300 ml
12. 2 l 500 ml
13. 2 l 650 ml
14. 1 l 850 ml
15. 1 l 900 ml
16. 4 l
17. 1 l 500 ml
18. 2 l 350 ml

---

page 10

Capacity M3

Litres and pints

1. 8 pints
2. 6 pints
3. 4 pints
4. 13 pints
5. 14 pints
6. 24 pints
7. 17 pints
8. 11 pints
9. 30 pints

10. 1 litre
11. 3·5 litres
12. 2 litres
13. 1·5 litres
14. 4·5 litres

e 10. $9 - 2 = 7$ 7 pints $\approx 3\frac{1}{2}$ litres
11. $9 - 7 = 2$ 2 pints $\approx$ 1 litre
12. $9 - 4 = 5$ 5 pints $\approx 2\frac{1}{2}$ litres
13. $9 - 3 = 6$ 6 pints $\approx$ 3 litres
14. $9 - 9 = 0$ 0 pints $\approx$ 0 litres

---

page 11

Capacity M3

Litres (l) and millilitres (ml)

1. 20 x 75p = 1500p = £15
2. 40 x 75p = 3000p = £30
3. 30 x 75p = 2250p = £22·50
4. 50 x 75p = 3750p = £37·50
5. 10 x 75p = 750p = £7·50
6. 100 x 75p = 7500p = £75
7. 110 x 75p = 8250p = £82·50

8. 1 + 3 + 3 + 3 + 2 = 12 doses 12 x 5 ml = 60 ml
9. 1000 ml – 200 ml = 800 ml 800 ml ÷ 4 = 200 ml each

---

page 12

Area M4

Area

1. $A = 15\ cm^2$
2. $A = 30\ cm^2$
3. $A = 20\ cm^2$
4. $A = 6\ cm^2$
5. $A = 3\ cm^2$
6. $A = 12\ cm^2$
7. $A = 12\ cm^2$

Shape, Data and Measures

page 12 cont ...

Area M4

8. $A = 14\ cm^2$ 9. $A = 9\ cm^2$ 10. $A = 8\ cm^2$ 11. $A = 12\ cm^2$
12. $A = 12\ cm^2$ 13. $A = 16\ cm^2$

---

page 13

Area M4

Area

1. $A = 11\ cm^2$ 2. $A = 18\ cm^2$ 3. $A = 8\ cm^2$ 4. $A = 7\ cm^2$
5. $A = 16\ cm^2$ 6. $A = 26\ cm^2$ 7. $A = 5\ cm^2$ 8. $A = 10\ cm^2$
9. $A = 13\ cm^2$

Explore

Answers will vary.

---

page 14

Area M4

Area

1. $A = 9\ cm^2$ 2. $A = 25\ cm^2$ 3. $A = 10\ cm^2$ 4. $A = 4\ cm^2$
5. $A = 13\ cm^2$ 6. $A = 31\ cm^2$ 7. $A = 24\ cm^2$ 8. $A = 22\ cm^2$

9. $8\ cm \times 5\ cm = 40\ cm^2$ $7\ cm \times 6\ cm = 42\ cm^2$ $42\ cm^2 - 40\ cm^2 = 2\ cm^2$
   difference in area is $2\ cm^2$
10. $3\ m \times 8\ m = 24\ m^2$ $24\ m^2 \times 4 = 96\ m^2$ $96\ m^2 \div 32\ m^2 = 3$
   Chris needs 3 tins

---

page 15

Perimeter M5

Perimeter and area

1. P = 8 cm 2. P = 8 cm 3. P = 12 cm 4. P = 14 cm
5. P = 10 cm 6. P = 16 cm 7. P = 12 cm 8. P = 12 cm
9. P = 16 cm 10. P = 14 cm

3 shapes with same perimeter are **3**, **7** and **8**.

● 1. $A = 3\ cm^2$ 2. $A = 4\ cm^2$ 3. $A = 5\ cm^2$ 4. $A = 6\ cm^2$
5. $A = 6\ cm^2$ 6. $A = 12\ cm^2$ 7. $A = 9\ cm^2$ 8. $A = 8\ cm^2$
9. $A = 7\ cm^2$ 10. $A = 10\ cm^2$

page 15 cont ...

Perimeter M5

Explore

square	perimeter (cm)	area (cm^2)
1 x 1	4	1
2 x 2	8	4
3 x 3	12	9
4 x 4	16	16
etc.		

The perimeter is the length of the sides multiplied by 4.
The area is the length of the sides multiplied by itself.
The 10th square will have perimeter 40 cm and area 100 cm^2.

page 16

Perimeter M5

Perimeter and area

1. P = 8 cm A = 3 cm^2
2. P = 12 cm A = 5 cm^2
3. P = 12 cm A = 5 cm^2
4. P = 12 cm A = 5 cm^2
5. P = 16 cm A = 7 cm^2
6. P = 12 cm A = 5 cm^2
7. P = 12 cm A = 5 cm^2
8. P = 12 cm A = 5 cm^2
9. P = 12 cm A = 5 cm^2

45 cm^2

Explore

Answers will vary.

page 17

Perimeter

Perimeter

1. 15 m x 2 = 30 m 5 m x 2 = 10 m perimeter = 40 m
2. 16 m x 2 = 32 m 10 m x 2 = 20 m perimeter = 52 m
3. 14 m x 2 = 28 m 5 m x 2 = 10 m perimeter = 38 m
4. 18 m x 2 = 36 m 5 m x 2 = 10 m perimeter = 46 m
5. 13 m x 2 = 26 m 10 m x 2 = 20 m perimeter = 46 m
6. 16 m x 2 = 32 m 8 m x 2 = 16 m perimeter = 48 m

Shape, Data and Measures

page 17 cont ...

Perimeter M5

1. 75 m^2 2. 160 m^2 3. 70 m^2 4. 90 m^2
5. 130 m^2 6. 128 m^2

7. 20 cm x 2 = 40 cm 30 cm x 2 = 60 cm 40 cm x 2 = 80 cm
50 cm x 2 = 100 cm 40 cm + 60 cm + 80 cm + 100 cm = 280 cm ribbon
8. Various possible answers e.g. 20 cm x 30 cm – dimensions must add to 50 cm

---

page 18

Time M6

Minutes

1. 13 minutes 2. 22 minutes 3. 52 minutes 4. 38 minutes
5. 33 minutes 6. 40 minutes 7. 42 minutes 8. 29 minutes
9. 57 minutes 10. 4 minutes 11. 18 minutes 12. 6 minutes
13. 14 minutes

1a. 47 minutes 2a. 38 minutes 3a. 8 minutes 4a. 22 minutes
5a. 27 minutes 6a. 20 minutes 7a. 18 minutes 8a. 31 minutes
9a. 3 minutes 10a. 56 minutes 11a. 42 minutes 12a. 54 minutes
13a. 46 minutes

---

page 19

Time M6

Telling the time

1. 20 past 9 2. 5 past 4 3. 14 minutes to 7
4. 3 minutes past 11 5. 10 minutes to 3 6. 27 minutes past 1
7. 4 minutes to 6 8. 27 minutes to 12 9. 21 minutes past 8

1. 9:20 2. 4:05 3. 6:46 4. 11:03 5. 2:50
6. 1:27 7. 5:56 8. 11:33 9. 8:21

10. 27 minutes 11. 34 minutes 12. 27 minutes

---

page 20

Time M6

Telling the time

1. 1 and f 2. 2 and d 3. 3 and a 4. 4 and c 5. 5 and g
6. 6 and b 7. 7 and e

Shape, Data and Measures

page 20 cont ...

Time M6

1. 5:35 2. 2:51 3. 4:11 4. 7:23 5. 7:04
6. 9:14 7. 5:57

8. 10 minutes + 42 minutes + 15 minutes = 67 minutes
   7:30 + 67 minutes = 8:37 Vijay gets to school at 8:37 a.m.
9. 90 minutes + 5 minutes = 95 minutes 9:10 + 95 minutes = 10:45
   Yes, Jess' film has been recorded.

---

page 21

Time M6

a.m. and p.m.

1. 7:20 a.m. 2. 11:20 a.m. 3. 3:45 p.m. 4. 1:35 p.m.
5. 4:45 a.m. 6. 12:15 a.m. 7. 2:15 p.m.

8–15. Answers will vary.

---

page 22

Time M7

Calendars

1. 6 November 2. 20 November 3. 23 November
4. 19 November

5. Sunday 6. Tuesday 7. Thursday 8. Wednesday

9. 8 days 10. 12 days 11. 16 days

---

page 23

Time M7

Calendars

1. 5 2. 4 3. 4 4. 4 5. 5

6. Tuesday 7. Monday 8. Saturday 9. Wednesday 10. Friday

11. Thursday 12. Sunday 13. Friday 14. Thursday 15. Tuesday
16. Sunday

17. January → 8 18. February → 8 19. March → 10
20. April → 8 21. May → 8 22. June → 10

Shape, Data and Measures

page 24

Time M7

Calendars

January, February, March, April, May, June, July, August, September, October, November, December

1. January 31 days
2. March 31 days
3. October 31 days
4. June 30 days
5. April 30 days
6. August 31 days
7. July 31 days
8. May 31 days
9. September 30 days
10. November 30 days
11. February 28 or 29 days
12. December 31 days

---

page 25

Time M8

Timetables

1. 10:30 **2.** 1:00 **3.** 11:30 **4.** 12:30
5. 9:00 **6.** 10:15 **7.** 9:50

1a. 11:30 **2a.** 1:10 **3a.** 12:30 **4a.** 1:00
5a. 9:20 **6a.** 10:30 **7a.** 10:15

8. Space Cops **9.** Strange Hill School **10.** News **11.** Bonzo the Dog

Programme	Length
Rab and Rob	20 minutes
Bonzo the Dog	30 minutes
Strange Hill School	25 minutes
Dragon Quest	15 minutes
Animal Watch	1 hour
Space Cops	1 hour
Brainiac Quiz	30 minutes
News	10 minutes

---

page 26

Time 

Timetables

1. 20 minutes **2.** 20 minutes **3.** 3 hours 30 minutes
4. 30 minutes

5. 4 hours **6.** 35 minutes **7.** 7 hours 45 minutes
8. 55 minutes **9.** 55 minutes

Shape, Data and Measures

page 27

Time M8

Timetables

1. 5 minutes
2. 1 hour 16 minutes
3. 1 hour 37 minutes
4. 2 hours 2 minutes

5. 1 hour 5 minutes
6. 6 minutes
7. 40 minutes
8. 1 hour 10 minutes
9. 27 minutes
10. 1 hour 37 minutes
11. 46 minutes
12. 48 minutes

Bus station	3:30
Supermarket	3:35
School	4:40
Town hall	4:46
Post office	4:52
Library	5:04
Hospital	5:07
Train station	5:12
Swimming pool	5:32
Bus station	5:40

Explore

From	To	Time
Bus station	Supermarket	5 minutes
Supermarket	School	1 hour 5 minutes
School	Town hall	6 minutes
Town hall	Post office	6 minutes
Post office	Library	12 minutes
Library	Hospital	3 minutes
Hospital	Train station	5 minutes
Train station	Swimming pool	20 minutes
Swimming pool	Bus station	8 minutes

page 27 cont ...

Time M8

Times in order	From	To
3 minutes	Library	Hospital
5 minutes	Bus station	Supermarket
5 minutes	Hospital	Train station
6 minutes	Town hall	Post office
6 minutes	School	Town hall
8 minutes	Swimming pool	Bus station
12 minutes	Post office	Library
20 minutes	Train station	Swimming pool
1 hour 5 minutes	Supermarket	School

The shortest journey is 3 minutes, from the library to the hospital.
The longest journey is 1 hour 5 minutes, from the supermarket to the school.

page 28

Time M9

Seconds

1. 20 seconds
2. 10 seconds
3. 35 seconds
4. 45 seconds
5. 15 seconds
6. 55 seconds
7. 30 seconds
8. 17 seconds
9. 39 seconds
10. 5 seconds
11. 8 seconds
12. 48 seconds
13. 50 seconds

1a. 40 seconds
2a. 50 seconds
3a. 25 seconds
4a. 15 seconds
5a. 45 seconds
6a. 5 seconds
7a. 30 seconds
8a. 43 seconds
9a. 21 seconds
10a. 55 seconds
11a. 52 seconds
12a. 12 seconds
13a. 10 seconds

page 29

Time M9

Seconds

1. 1 minute 15 seconds
2. 1 minute 32 seconds
3. 1 minute 50 seconds
4. 1 minute 36 seconds
5. 2 minutes 10 seconds
6. 2 minutes 5 seconds
7. 1 minute 31 seconds
8. 2 minutes 2 seconds
9. 1 minute 24 seconds

page 29 cont ...

Time M9

10. Raj, Ben, Jess, Fi
11. Mani, Marcos
12. nobody
13. Bec, Tim
14. Jill
15. Raj
16. Ben
17. Mani

Raj, Jess, Ben, Fi, Mani, Marcos, Tim, Bec, Jill

---

page 30

Time M9

Seconds

1. 80 seconds
2. 65 seconds
3. 100 seconds
4. 67 seconds
5. 112 seconds
6. 132 seconds
7. 130 seconds
8. 95 seconds
9. 140 seconds
10. 160 seconds

11. 40 seconds — 4 points
12. 1 minute 20 seconds — 8 points
13. 1 minute 50 seconds — 11 points
14. 3 minutes — 18 points
15. 2 minutes 30 seconds — 15 points
16. 2 minutes — 12 points
17. 4 minutes 30 seconds — 27 points

Explore

5 minutes = 300 seconds
half an hour = 1800 seconds
an hour = 3600 seconds

Answers will vary.

---

page 31

Time M9

Seconds

1. 150 seconds
2. 55 seconds
3. 200 seconds
4. 30 seconds
5. 240 seconds
6. 10 seconds
7. 1000 seconds

8. 10 minutes = 600 seconds $600 \div 30 = 20$ $600 \div 60 = 10$
   largest number of games possible 20; fewest games possible 10
9. 600 seconds = 10 minutes; puppies born at 10:20, 10:30, 10:40, 10:50, 11:00
   last puppy born at 11:00

Shape, Data and Measures

page 32

2-d shape **S1**

Polygons

1. yes triangle
2. yes rectangle
3. yes hexagon
4. no ellipse or oval
5. yes pentagon
6. yes square
7. yes hexagon
8. no semicircle
9. yes triangle
10. no circle
11. no
12. yes hexagon
13. yes kite or quadrilateral

Answers as above.

---

page 33

2-d shape **S1**

Naming polygons

1. octagon, 8
2. square, 4
3. octagon, 8
4. pentagon, 5
5. triangle, 3
6. hexagon, 6
7. rectangle, 4
8. triangle, 3
9. heptagon, 7
10. hexagon, 6
11. hexagon, 6
12. pentagon, 5
13. rectangle, 4

14–19. Answers will vary.

---

page 34

2-d shape **S2**

Naming polygons

1. pentagon, rectangle
2. square, triangle
3. hexagon, heptagon
4. hexagon, quadrilateral
5. octagon, triangle
6. heptagon, pentagon
7. triangle, hexagon
8. quadrilateral, octagon
9. pentagon, square

10–14. Answers will vary.

---

page 35

2-d shape **S2**

Regular polygons

1. yes, regular hexagon
2. yes, square
3. no, triangle
4. no, hexagon
5. yes, regular (equilateral) triangle
6. no, pentagon

Shape, Data and Measures

page 35 cont ...

2-d shape S2

7. yes, regular octagon
8. no, rectangle
9. yes, regular pentagon
10. no, hexagon
11. no, triangle
12. no, octagon
13 no, quadrilateral (kite)

Explore

Answers will vary.

---

page 36

2-d shape S2

Isosceles and equilateral triangles

1. equilateral	2. isosceles	3. equilateral	4. isosceles
5. isosceles	6. equilateral	7. equilateral	8. isosceles
9. isosceles	10. equilateral	11. equilateral	

---

page 37

2-d shape S2

Isosceles triangles

1. no	2. yes	3. no	4. no	5. yes
6. no	7. yes	8. no	9. no	

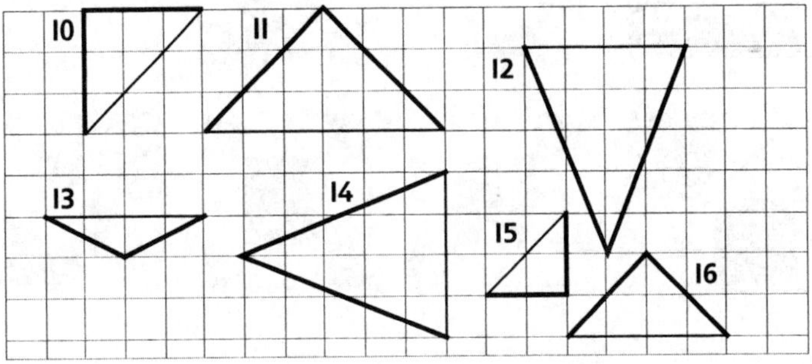

10 11 12 13 14 15 16

---

page 38

Symmetry S3

Symmetry

1. yes	2. no	3. no	4. yes	5. yes
6. no	7. yes	8. yes	9. yes	10. yes
11. no	12. no			

Explore

Answers will vary.

Shape, Data and Measures

page 39

Symmetry **S3**

Symmetry

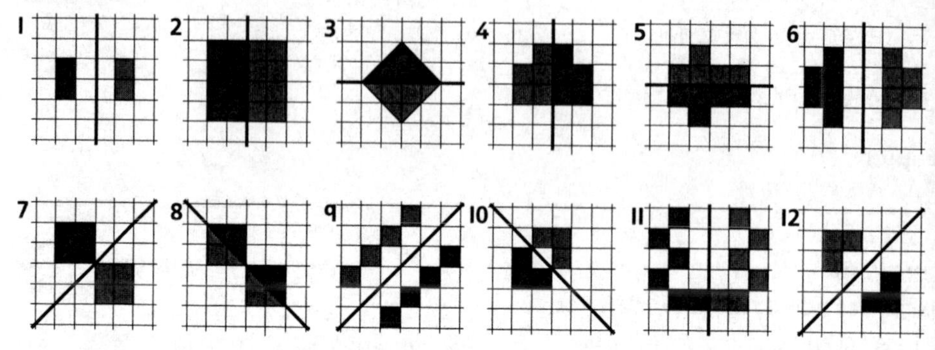

Answers will vary.

---

page 40

Symmetry **S3**

Symmetrical patterns

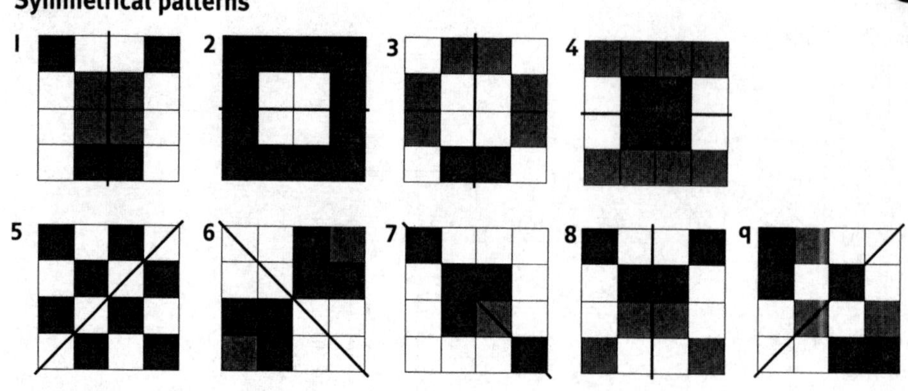

Explore

Answers will vary.

---

page 41

3-d shape **S4**

Nets

1. yes **2.** no **3.** yes **4.** no **5.** yes

6. no **7.** yes **8.** no **9.** yes

Shape, Data and Measures

page 42

3-d shape S4

Nets

1. cube
2. tetrahedron or triangular-based pyramid
3. cuboid
4. square-based pyramid
5. triangular prism
6. pentagonal prism
7. cuboid or square prism
8. cube
9. pentagonal-based pyramid
10. hexagonal prism

Answers will vary.

1a. 6	**b.** 8	**c.** 12	**2a.** 4	**b.** 4	**c.** 6
3a. 6	**b.** 8	**c.** 12	**4a.** 5	**b.** 5	**c.** 8
5a. 5	**b.** 6	**c.** 9	**6a.** 7	**b.** 10	**c.** 15
7a. 6	**b.** 8	**c.** 12	**8a.** 6	**b.** 8	**c.** 12
9a. 6	**b.** 6	**c.** 10	**10a.** 8	**b.** 12	**c.** 18

page 43

3-d shape S4

Prisms and pyramids

1. prism
2. pyramid
3. prism
4. pyramid
5. pyramid
6. prism
7. prism
8. prism
9. pyramid
10. pyramid

2a. square-based
4a. triangular-based
5a. pentagonal-based
9a. triangular-based
10a. hexagonal-based

4 and 9 are tetrahedra

page 44

Direction S5

Compass points

1. east
2. south
3. south-west
4. north
5. north-east
6. west
7. south-east
8. north-east
9. north-west
10. south-east
11. south-west
12. south

1a. west
2a. north
3a. north-east
4a. south
5a. south-west
6a. east
7a. north-west
8a. south-west
9a. south-east
10a. north-west
11a. north-east
12a. north

Explore

east and west
north-east and south-west
south-east and north-west

Shape, Data and Measures

page 45

Direction S5

Compass points

1. south
2. north
3. east
4. west
5. south-east

6. east
7. south-east
8. north
9. west
10. south
11. north-east

12. east
13. south-west
14. north-west
15. west
16. north-east
17. north

---

page 46

Direction S5

Compass points

1. north-east
2. east
3. north-east
4. north
5. south
6. north-west
7. north-east
8. south-west
9. south-east

e Answers will vary.

Explore
Answers will vary.

---

page 47

Angle S6

Turning

1. north to south-east
2. east to north
3. west to north-east
4. south to north-west
5. south-west to east
6. south-east to north-east
7. north-west to south-east
8. north to south-east
9. south to north-east

1a. $1\frac{1}{2}$ right angles
2a. 3 right angles
3a. $1\frac{1}{2}$ right angles
4a. $2\frac{1}{2}$ right angles
5a. $1\frac{1}{2}$ right angles
6a. 1 right angle
7a. 2 right angles
8a. $2\frac{1}{2}$ right angles
9a. $2\frac{1}{2}$ right angles

Shape, Data and Measures

page 48

Angle **S6**

Angles

1. north to south
2. west to north
3. north-east to south-west
4. south to north-east
5. east to north-west
6. north-west to north
7. north to west
8. south-east to north-east
9. west to north-west
10. south-west to west

1a. clockwise **2a.** clockwise **3a.** clockwise
4a. anticlockwise **5a.** clockwise **6a.** clockwise
7a. clockwise **8a.** anticlockwise **9a.** clockwise
10a. anticlockwise

Explore

Answers will vary.

---

page 49

Angle **S6**

Angles

1. half past 12
2. 20 to 5
3. 8 o'clock
4. quarter to 10
5. 10 to 3
6. 10 past 5
7. half past 11
8. 10 to 10
9. 25 to 9
10. 10 to 2

11. $1\frac{1}{3}$ right angles = 120°
12. $\frac{1}{3}$ right angle = 30°
13. 2 right angles = 180°
14. 3 right angles = 270°
15. $\frac{2}{3}$ right angle = 60°
16. $2\frac{1}{3}$ right angles = 210°
17. 1 right angle = 90°
18. $3\frac{1}{3}$ right angles = 300°

---

page 50

Position **S7**

Coordinates

1. 5 **2.** 2 **3.** 3 **4.** 6 **5.** 0
6. 1 **7.** 2 **8.** 4 **9.** 5

1a. 1 **2a.** 3 **3a.** 5 **4a.** 3 **5a.** 4
6a. 5 **7a.** 0 **8a.** 2 **9a.** 6

1b. (5,1) **2b.** (2,3) **3b.** (3,5) **4b.** (6,3) **5b.** (0,4)
6b. (1,5) **7b.** (2,0) **8b.** (4,2) **9b.** (5,6)

Shape, Data and Measures

page 51

Position S7

Coordinates

1. (1,1) 2. (5,5) 3. (8,6) 4. (9,9) 5. (9,2)
6. (2,3) 7. (0,4) 8. (5,1) 9. (4,7) 10. (2,6)

---

page 52

Position S7

Coordinates

1. roundabout 2. oak tree 3. bench 4. slide
5. see-saw 6. pond 7. gate 8. café
9. sand pit 10. swings

11. roundabout 12. sand pit 13. bench

---

page 53

Frequency tables D1

Frequency tables

vowel	total
a	12
e	8
i	7
o	6
u	1

1. i 2. o 3. a 4. u 5. a 6. e

7. e, 1 more 8. e, 7 more 9. i, 1 more 10. o, 5 more
11. a, 4 more 12. a, 11 more

Explore
Answers will vary.

---

page 54

Frequency tables D1

Frequency tables

1. Junior Street 2. Clever Class 3. The Odd Family
4. Animals, animals 5. The Odd Family 6. Space Cops

7. 10 8. 30 9. 15 10. 45 11. 40 12. 37

Explore
Answers will vary.

Shape, Data and Measures

page 55

Frequency tables **D1**

Frequency tables

number	frequency
0	2
1	5
2	8
3	6
4	7
5	3
6	4
7	3
8	3
9	1

1. twice **2.** 3 times **3.** 3 times **4.** once
5. 5 times **6.** 2 **7.** 9 **8.** 1
9. 6 **10.** 3 **11.** 2 **12.** 9
13. 8

Explore

Answers will vary.

---

page 56

Pictographs **D2**

Pictographs

1. April **2.** July **3.** 7 **4.** 21 **5.** 14 **6.** 6
7. 45 **8.** 13 **9.** 17 **10.** 8 **11.** 7

Days it didn't rain, March to July

March
April
Months
May
June
July

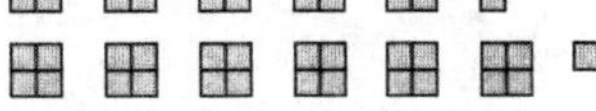

key = 4 days

Number of days

Shape, Data and Measures

page 57

Pictographs **D2**

Pictographs

1. United, Rovers and Town
2. City and Rangers
3. 20 – 18 = 2 2 goals
4. 20 – 7 = 13 13 goals
5. 20 – 14 = 6 6 goals
6. 20 – 10 = 10 10 goals
7. 28 goals
8. 33 goals
9. 68 goals

Explore

Answers will vary.

---

page 58

Pictographs **D2**

Pictographs

1. 19
2. 15
3. 16
4. 11
5. 14
6. red, blue, black
7. yellow, pink
8. 33
9. 31
10. 64
11. 61
12. 56
13. red
14. black

Colours of sweets in a packet

Colour: red, blue, yellow, black, pink

key = 3 sweets

Number of sweets

---

page 59

Bar graphs **D3**

Bar graphs

1. 10
2. 0
3. 8
4. 7
5. 13
6. 10
7. 3
8. 13
9. cat, fish
10. dog, rabbit, mouse
11. dog, rabbit, hamster
12. cat, fish, hamster

Explore

Answers will vary.

Shape, Data and Measures

page 60

Bar graphs **D3**

Bar graphs

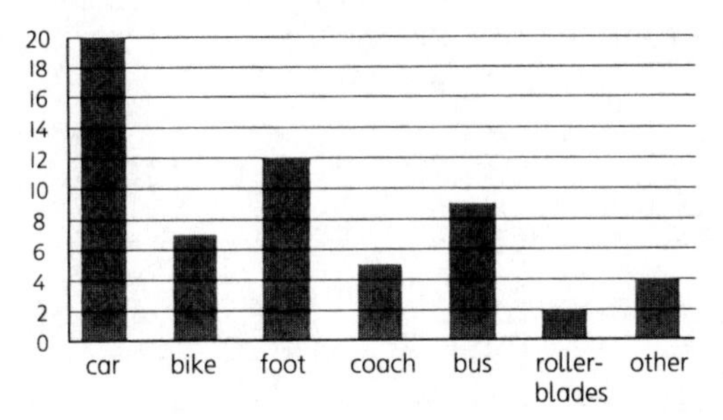

1. 25 **2.** 16 **3.** 14 **4.** 14 **5.** 5
6. 15 **7.** 11 **8.** 4 **9.** 13

---

page 61

Bar graphs **D3**

Bar graphs

1. 55 **2.** 40 **3.** 50 **4.** 15
5. Thursday **6.** Wednesday **7.** 75 **8.** 70
9. 90 **10.** 120 **11.** 195

---

page 62

Sorting diagrams **D4**

Venn diagrams

1. Ben, Mandy, Sophie
2. Ben, Mandy, Rikki, Sumi
3. Ben, Mandy
4. Sophie
5. Rikki, Sumi
6. Dan, Guy
7.

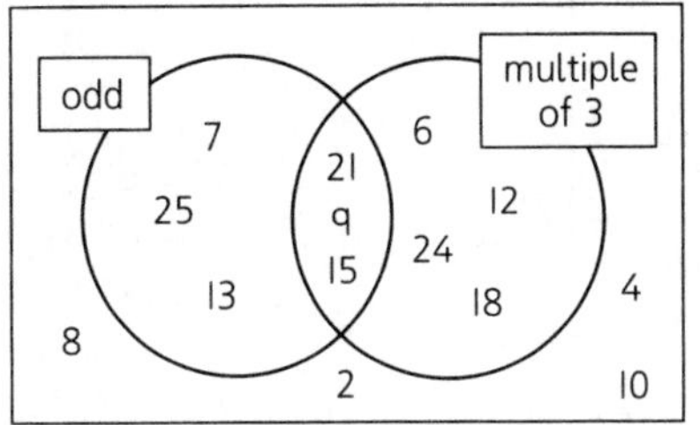

8.

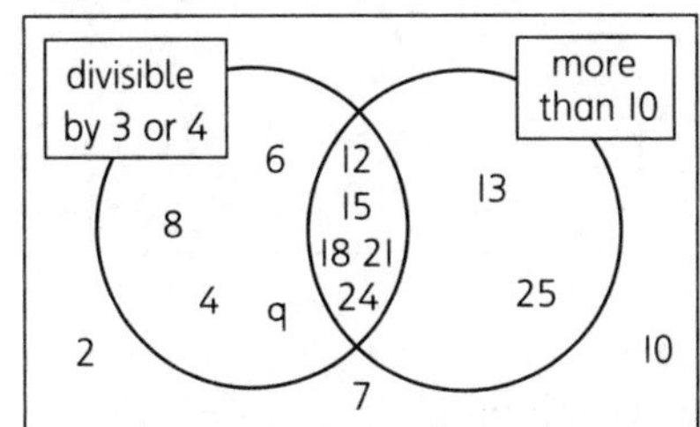

Shape, Data and Measures

page 63

Sorting diagrams **D4**

Carroll diagrams

1. Jon, Suzie, Amit
2. Jon, Suzie, Karen, Sean, Ruth
3. Karen, Sean, Ruth, Matt, Beni
4. Karen, Sean, Ruth
5. Amit
6. Jon, Suzie
7. Matt, Beni

8.

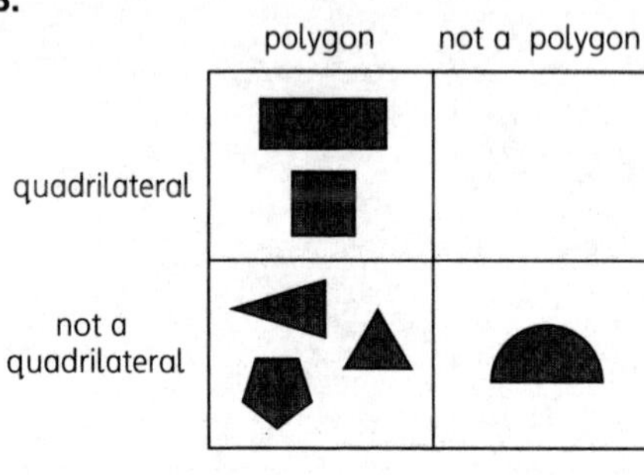

9.

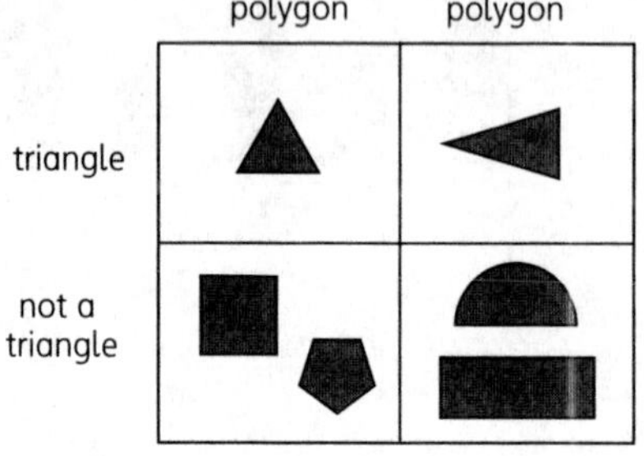

---

page 64

Sorting diagrams **D4**

Sorting diagrams

1.

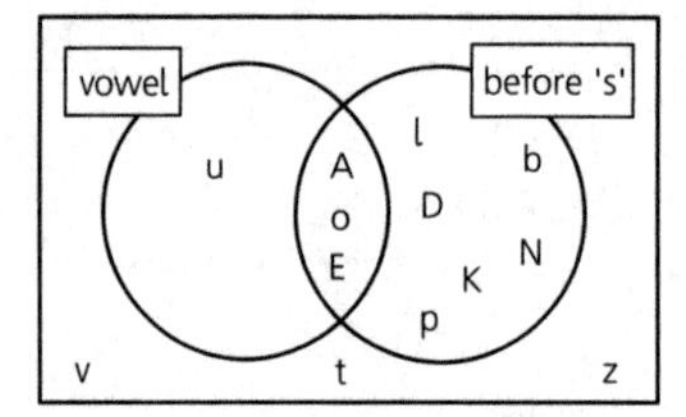

2.

	capital	not a capital
vowel	A E	u o
not a vowel	K N D	b z t v l p

3.

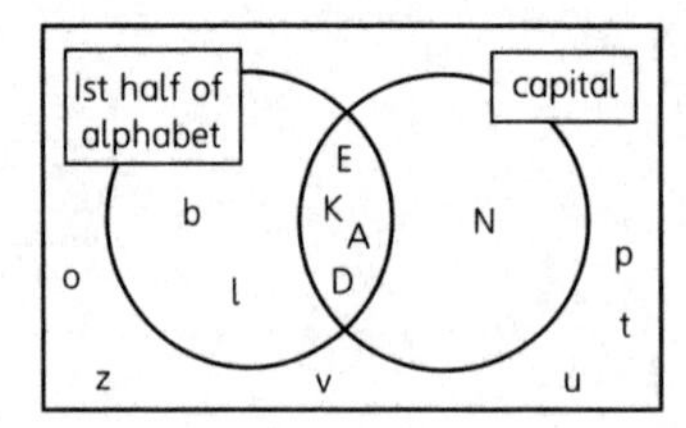

4.

	before 'j'	not before 'j'
capital	A D E	K N
not a capital	b	z t v l p u o

Explore

Answers will vary.

Photocopy Masters

Page 1

Place-value N1

4-digit numbers

1. 4372 **2.** 2679 **3.** 4852 **4.** 7374 **5.** 7562
6. 4039 **7.** 7903 **8.** 2850 **9.** 7003 **10.** 6080
11. 4552 **12.** 3974 **13.** 4516

Page 2

Place-value 

4-digit numbers

4265 8571 3206 4057 3980

Page 4

Addition/subtraction N2

Adding to 10 and 20

1. 1 + 9 = 10 **2.** 3 + 7 = 10 **3.** 4 + 6 = 10
4. 8 + 2 = 10 **5.** 7 + 3 = 10 **6.** 4 + 6 = 10
7. 0 + 10 = 10 **8.** 1 + 9 = 10 **9.** 8 + 2 = 10
10. 3 + 7 = 10 **11.** 5 + 5 = 10 **12.** 10 + 0 = 10
13. 9 + 11 = 20 **14.** 15 + 5 = 20 **15.** 12 + 8 = 20
16. 11 + 9 = 20 **17.** 6 + 14 = 20 **18.** 10 + 10 = 20
19. 8 + 12 = 20 **20.** 18 + 2 = 20 **21.** 13 + 7 = 20
22. 7 + 13 = 20 **23.** 3 + 17 = 20 **24.** 14 + 6 = 20

Page 6

Addition/subtraction N2

Adding to the next ten

1. 27 + 3 = 30 **2.** 56 + 4 = 60 **3.** 43 + 7 = 50
4. 33 + 7 = 40 **5.** 44 + 6 = 50 **6.** 79 + 1 = 80
7. 115 + 5 = 120 **8.** 94 + 6 = 100 **9.** 89 + 1 = 90
10. 65 + 5 = 70 **11.** 81 + 9 = 90 **12.** 52 + 8 = 60
13. 36 + 4 = 40 **14.** 108 + 2 = 110 **15.** 62 + 8 = 70
16. 11 + 9 = 20 **17.** 97 + 3 = 100 **18.** 74 + 6 = 80
19. 128 + 2 = 130 **20.** 137 + 3 = 140

Page 7

Addition/subtraction 

Differences

1. 121 – 117 = 4 **2.** 112 – 106 = 6 **3.** 134 – 129 = 5
4. 125 – 118 = 7 **5.** 111 – 105 = 6 **6.** 135 – 127 = 8
7. 124 – 119 = 5 **8.** 122 – 116 = 6 **9.** 143 – 137 = 6
10. 113 – 107 = 6 **11.** 131 – 126 = 5 **12.** 142 – 135 = 7

Photocopy Masters

Page 7 cont ...

Addition/subtraction N3

13. 127 – 118 = 9 **14.** 121 – 113 = 8 **15.** 114 – 106 = 8
16. 132 – 125 = 7 **17.** 146 – 137 = 9

Page 9

Addition/subtraction N4

Adding to 100

75 + 25 = 100
15 + 85 = 100
5 + 95 = 100
65 + 35 = 100
30 + 70 = 100
80 + 20 = 100
40 + 60 = 100
50 + 50 = 100
90 + 10 = 100
45 + 55 = 100

Page 10

Addition/subtraction N4

Adding to 100

1. 26 shaded + 74 unshaded = 100
2. 37 shaded + 63 unshaded = 100
3. 44 shaded + 56 unshaded = 100
4. 19 shaded + 81 unshaded = 100
5. 52 shaded + 48 unshaded = 100
6. 86 shaded + 14 unshaded = 100
7. 32 shaded + 68 unshaded = 100
8. 71 shaded + 29 unshaded = 100

Page 11

Addition/subtraction N4

Adding to 100

1. 23 + 77 = 100
2. 80 + 20 = 100
3. 51 + 49 = 100
4. 64 + 36 = 100
5. 81 + 19 = 100
6. 64 + 36 = 100
7. 35 + 65 = 100
8. 55 + 45 = 100
9. 8 + 92 = 100
10. 69 + 31 = 100
11. 53 + 47 = 100
12. 70 + 30 = 100
13. 72 + 28 = 100
14. 93 + 7 = 100
15. 56 + 44 = 100
16. 82 + 18 = 100
17. 29 + 71 = 100
18. 28 + 72 = 100

Page 13

Addition/subtraction 

Adding several numbers

9	3	5	7	2	26
6	5	4	9	1	25
5	2	8	3	8	26
3	7	9	6	5	30
9	8	6	4	7	34
32	25	32	29	23	

Photocopy Masters

Page 13 cont ...

Addition/subtraction N5

7	9	5	13	9	43
4	9	8	6	12	39
5	11	3	9	7	35
9	8	12	7	13	49
6	9	7	11	4	37
31	46	35	46	45	

Page 14

Properties of number N6

Counting in 1s, 10s, 25s and 50s

1. 50	60	70	80	**2.** 350	400	450	500
3. 150	125	100	75	**4.** 168	169	170	171
5. 600	550	500	450	**6.** 225	250	275	300
7. 180	179	178	177	**8.** 550	650	750	850
9. 322	372	422	472	**10.** 760	710	660	610

Page 15

Properties of number N6

Counting

Answers will vary.

Page 16

Multiplication/division N7

Multiplying

1. A and F 3 x 5 = 5 x 3 = 15
2. B and H 3 x 7 = 7 x 3 = 21
3. C and I 2 x 9 = 9 x 2 = 18
4. D and J 8 x 4 = 4 x 8 = 32
5. E and G 4 x 6 = 6 x 4 = 24

Page 17

Multiplication/division N7

Multiplying

1. 2 x 30 = 60, 30 x 2 = 60
2. 4 x 20 = 80, 20 x 4 = 80
3. 3 x 40 = 120, 40 x 3 = 120
4. 5 x 20 = 100, 20 x 5 = 100
5. 4 x 25 = 100, 25 x 4 = 100
6. 3 x 20 = 60, 20 x 3 = 60

Photocopy Masters

Page 17 cont ...

Multiplication/division N7

7. 2 x 40 = 80, 40 x 2 = 80
8. 4 x 30 = 120, 30 x 4 = 120
9. 2 x 60 = 120, 60 x 2 = 120
10. 3 x 50 = 150, 50 x 3 = 150
11. 6 x 25 = 150, 25 x 6 = 150
12. 5 x 40 = 200, 40 x 5 = 200

Page 18

Multiplication/division N8

Dividing

1. 12 ÷ 2 = 6
2. 15 ÷ 3 = 5
3. 16 ÷ 4 = 4
4. 10 ÷ 5 = 2
5. 27 ÷ 3 = 9
6. 20 ÷ 2 = 10
7. 15 ÷ 5 = 3
8. 30 ÷ 5 = 6
9. 20 ÷ 5 = 4

Page 19

Multiplication/division N8

Dividing

1. 12 ÷ 2 = 6
2. 15 ÷ 3 = 5
3. 8 ÷ 4 = 2
4. 10 ÷ 5 = 2
5. 12 ÷ 6 = 2
6. 21 ÷ 7 = 3
7. 40 ÷ 8 = 5
8. 16 ÷ 2 = 8
9. 50 ÷ 10 = 5
10. 16 ÷ 4 = 4
11. 9 ÷ 3 = 3
12. 18 ÷ 9 = 2
13. 24 ÷ 8 = 3
14. 8 ÷ 2 = 4
15. 15 ÷ 5 = 3
16. 18 ÷ 6 = 3
17. 30 ÷ 3 = 10
18. 90 ÷ 10 = 9
19. 20 ÷ 4 = 5
20. 35 ÷ 7 = 5

Page 20

Multiplication/division

Problem page

1. 32 ÷ 4 = 8 8 biscuits
2. 48 ÷ 6 = 8 8 rows
3. 45 ÷ 5 = 9 9 piles
4. 1 pile of 28 2 piles of 14 14 piles of 2 4 piles of 7 7 piles of 4
5. 3 x 6 = 18 18
6. 2 (32) or 6 (36)
7. 12 or 24
8. 5 x 6 = 30 30 marbles

Page 21

Multiplication/division N9

Threes and fours

- 12, 24, 36, 48, 60

Photocopy Masters

Page 24

Multiplication/division **N10**

Halving

5	12	9
8	10	6
11	7	13

31	14	41
25	32	21
12	24	33

16	44	35
42	32	26
37	28	19

Page 25

Multiplication/division **N10**

Doubling

17 pairs
1, 2   2, 4   3, 6   4, 8   5, 10   6, 12   7, 14   8, 16   9, 18   13, 26   14, 28   15, 30
16, 32   17, 34   18, 36   19, 38   23, 46

Page 26

Multiplication/division **N11**

Eights

1	2	3	4	5	6	7	8	9	10
11	12	13	14	15	16	17	18	19	20
21	22	23	24	25	26	27	28	29	30
31	32	33	34	35	36	37	38	39	40
41	42	43	44	45	46	47	48	49	50
51	52	53	54	55	56	57	58	59	60
61	62	63	64	65	66	67	68	69	70
71	72	73	74	75	76	77	78	79	80
81	82	83	84	85	86	87	88	89	90
91	92	93	94	95	96	97	98	99	100

Answers will vary.

Photocopy Masters

Page 28

Multiplication/division N11

Fours and eights

1. 10 x 8 = 80
2. 9 x 8 = 72
3. 5 x 4 = 20   5 x 8 = 40
4. 7 x 4 = 28   7 x 8 = 56
5. 20 x 8 = 160
6. 30 x 8 = 240
7. 15 x 8 = 120
8. 100 x 4 = 400   100 x 8 = 800
9. 14 x 8 = 112
10. 25 x 8 = 200

Page 29

Fractions/decimals N12

Fractions

1. shaded $\frac{5}{6}$, clear $\frac{1}{6}$
2. shaded $\frac{3}{4}$, clear $\frac{1}{4}$
3. shaded $\frac{1}{3}$, clear $\frac{2}{3}$
4. shaded $\frac{3}{8}$, clear $\frac{5}{8}$
5. shaded $\frac{4}{6}$, clear $\frac{2}{6}$
6. shaded $\frac{3}{12}$, clear $\frac{9}{12}$
7. shaded $\frac{7}{8}$, clear $\frac{1}{8}$
8. shaded $\frac{4}{9}$, clear $\frac{5}{9}$

Page 30

Fractions/decimals N12

Fractions

Answers will vary.

Page 31

Fractions/decimals 

Fractions

1. $\frac{3}{8}$
2. $\frac{6}{8}$
3. $\frac{3}{8}$
4. $\frac{5}{8}$
5. $\frac{2}{8}$
6. $\frac{5}{8}$
7. $\frac{4}{8}$
8. $\frac{2}{8}$
9. $\frac{4}{8}$
10. $\frac{3}{8}$

Page 32

Fractions/decimals N13

Matching fractions

1. $\frac{1}{2} = \frac{2}{4}$
2. $\frac{1}{3} = \frac{2}{6}$
3. $\frac{2}{3} = \frac{4}{6}$
4. $\frac{1}{4} = \frac{2}{8}$
5. $\frac{1}{2} = \frac{3}{6}$
6. $\frac{3}{4} = \frac{6}{8}$
7. $\frac{3}{5} = \frac{6}{10}$
8. $\frac{1}{2} = \frac{4}{8}$

Photocopy Masters

Page 33

Fractions/decimals **N13**

Matching fractions

1. $\frac{1}{2} = \frac{2}{4}$
2. $1 = \frac{4}{4}$
3. $\frac{1}{2} = \frac{4}{8}$
4. $\frac{1}{8} = \frac{2}{16}$
5. $\frac{8}{8} = 1$
6. $\frac{2}{4} = \frac{4}{8}$
7. $\frac{4}{16} = \frac{1}{4}$
8. $\frac{1}{4} = \frac{2}{8}$
9. $\frac{1}{2} = \frac{8}{16}$
10. $\frac{2}{2} = 1$
11. $\frac{3}{4} = \frac{6}{8}$
12. $\frac{3}{4} = \frac{12}{16}$

Page 34

Fractions/decimals **N13**

Matching fractions

13 pairs

$\frac{1}{2} = \frac{2}{4} = \frac{3}{6} = \frac{4}{8} = \frac{5}{10}$

$\frac{1}{4} = \frac{2}{8}$

$\frac{2}{3} = \frac{4}{6} = \frac{6}{9}$

$\frac{3}{5} = \frac{6}{10}$

$\frac{1}{3} = \frac{2}{6} = \frac{3}{9}$

$\frac{1}{5} = \frac{2}{10}$

$\frac{2}{5} = \frac{4}{10}$

$\frac{4}{5} = \frac{8}{10}$

Page 35

Addition/subtraction **N14**

Adding near multiples of 10

+	26	41	17	52	33	67
19	45	60	36	71	52	86
12	38	53	29	64	45	79
39	65	80	56	91	72	106
21	47	62	38	73	54	88

+	252	173	86	345	64	147
31	283	204	117	376	95	178
49	301	222	135	394	113	196
22	274	195	108	367	86	169
59	311	232	145	404	123	206

Page 36

Addition/subtraction **N14**

Problem page

1. 83p – 19p = 64p
2. 132 + 9 = 141 pages

3. £22 + £29 = £51
4. 235 + 39 + 22 = 296 points

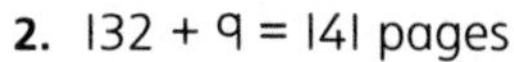

5. 44 – 29 = 15 15 years old
6. 72 + 19 = 91
7. 90 – 29 – 43 = 18
8. 10:51 a.m.

Photocopy Masters

Page 37

Addition/subtraction N15

Adding and subtracting multiples of 10

1. 60 + 30 = 90
2. 70 – 20 = 50
3. 120 + 50 = 170
4. 160 – 40 = 120
5. 270 – 30 = 240
6. 70 + 210 = 280
7. 250 – 120 = 130
8. 130 + 140 = 270
9. 320 + 140 = 460
10. 670 – 340 = 330
11. 80 + 70 = 150
12. 130 – 60 = 70
13. 150 + 90 = 240
14. 220 – 70 = 150
15. 370 + 140 = 510
16. 530 – 270 = 260

Page 38

Addition/subtraction 

Adding and subtracting multiples of 10

1. 200 + 300 = 500
2. 900 – 500 = 400
3. 1400 + 500 = 1900
4. 1700 – 300 = 1400
5. 300 + 2400 = 2700
6. 2600 – 400 = 2200
7. 4600 – 1500 = 3100
8. 3500 + 1300 = 4800
9. 5200 + 2400 = 7600
10. 7700 – 3500 = 4200
11. 1200 – 700 = 500
12. 700 + 800 = 1500
13. 2500 + 600 = 3100
14. 3100 – 700 = 2400
15. 6200 – 1700 = 4500
16. 4800 + 1500 = 6300

Page 39

Place-value N16

4-digit numbers

1. 2553 2563 2573
2. 4261 4271 4281
3. 6849 6859 6869
4. 3510 3520 3530
5. 5393 5403 5413
6. 7018 7028 7038
7. 3997 4007 4017
8. 3582 3592 3602
9. 3961 3971 3981
10. 2689 2699 2709

Photocopy Masters

Page 40

Place-value N16

4-digit numbers

	1 less	10 more	100 less	1000 more
3728	3727	3738	3628	4728
5462	5461	5472	5362	6462
7531	7530	7541	7431	8531
4089	4088	4099	3989	5089
2971	2970	2981	2871	3971
3296	3295	3306	3196	4296
2504	2503	2514	2404	3504
3098	3097	3108	2998	4098
9501	9500	9511	9401	10501
2309	2308	2319	2209	3309
4095	4094	4105	3995	5095
6200	6199	6210	6100	7200

Page 41

Addition/subtraction N17

Adding

1. 23 + 15 + 31 = 69
2. 26 + 32 + 14 = 72
3. 17 + 25 + 34 = 76
4. 46 + 18 + 25 = 89
5. 42 + 37 + 9 = 88
6. 15 + 28 + 17 = 60
7. 52 + 16 + 23 = 91
8. 35 + 21 + 29 = 85
9. 52 + 46 + 37 = 135
10. 48 + 63 + 59 = 170

Page 43

Addition/subtraction N17

Adding

1. 23 + 31 + 24 = 16 + 27 + 35 = 78
2. 15 + 16 + 27 = 58
3. 23 + 16 + 24 = 63
4. 31 + 42 + 35 = 108
5. 24 + 27 + 35 = 86
6. 23 + 15 + 31 = 69
7. 23 + 24 + 35 = 31 + 16 + 35 = 31 + 24 + 27 = 82

Photocopy Masters

Page 44

Addition/subtraction N18

Adding

1. 7 + 10 = 17
2. 18 + 10 = 28
3. 25 + 10 = 35
4. 34 + 10 = 44
5. 72 + 10 = 82
6. 23 + 10 = 33
7. 46 + 10 = 56
8. 37 + 10 = 47
9. 58 + 10 = 68
10. 89 + 10 = 99
11. 16 + 20 = 36
12. 27 + 20 = 47
13. 9 + 20 = 29
14. 35 + 20 = 55
15. 43 + 20 = 63
16. 79 + 20 = 99
17. 38 + 20 = 58
18. 52 + 20 = 72
19. 64 + 20 = 84
20. 85 + 20 = 105

Page 45

Addition/subtraction N18

Adding

1. 235 + 40 = 275
2. 326 + 20 = 346
3. 426 + 30 = 456
4. 635 + 50 = 685
5. 615 + 60 = 675
6. 346 + 20 = 366
7. 245 + 10 = 255
8. 954 + 30 = 984
9. 532 + 60 = 592
10. 183 + 10 = 193
11. 928 + 50 = 978
12. 715 + 80 = 795
13. 251 + 40 = 291
14. 305 + 40 = 345
15. 763 + 20 = 783
16. 542 + 30 = 572
17. 854 + 10 = 864
18. 109 + 70 = 179
19. 429 + 30 = 459
20. 858 + 20 = 878

Page 46

Addition/subtraction N19

Subtracting

1. 50p – 32p = 18p
2. 50p – 27p = 23p
3. 50p – 8p = 42p
4. 50p – 42p = 8p
5. 50p – 16p = 34p
6. 50p – 21p = 29p
7. 50p – 39p = 11p
8. 50p – 15p = 35p

Page 47

Addition/subtraction N19

Subtracting

1. 23 – 15 = 8
2. 32 – 16 = 16
3. 41 – 24 = 17
4. 54 – 36 = 18
5. 65 – 58 = 7
6. 73 – 41 = 32
7. 84 – 53 = 31
8. 95 – 62 = 33
9. 36 – 29 = 7
10. 42 – 35 = 7
11. 75 – 68 = 7
12. 29 – 17 = 12
13. 86 – 43 = 43
14. 52 – 19 = 33
15. 64 – 49 = 15
16. 31 – 16 = 15
17. 92 – 59 = 33
18. 44 – 18 = 26
19. 55 – 39 = 16
20. 71 – 28 = 43

Photocopy Masters

Page 48

Addition/subtraction N20

Subtracting

1. 21 − 13 = 8	**2.** 83 − 6 = 77	**3.** 42 − 37 = 5
4. 51 − 45 = 6	**5.** 72 − 58 = 14	**6.** 74 − 65 = 9
7. 80 − 66 = 14	**8.** 93 − 78 = 15	**9.** 63 − 38 = 25
10. 42 − 8 = 34	**11.** 72 − 47 = 25	**12.** 35 − 16 = 19
13. 31 − 9 = 22	**14.** 84 − 48 = 36	**15.** 54 − 29 = 25
16. 61 − 7 = 54	**17.** 65 − 8 = 57	**18.** 83 − 29 = 54
19. 94 − 35 = 59	**20.** 122 − 86 = 36	

Page 49

Addition/subtraction N20

Problem page

1. 46 − 19 = 27 27 marbles

2. 38 − 21 = 17 17 years old

3. 46 − 7 = 39 39 days

4. 54 − 28 = 26 26 days

5. 33 − 16 = 17 17 girls

6. 52 − 19 = 33 33 weeks

7. 33 + 9 = 42 half of 42 = 21 the number is 21

8. 23 and 9

Page 50

Properties of number N21

Threes and fours

1.	3	6	9	12	15	18	21	24	27	30
2.	12	15	18	21	24	27	30	33	36	39
3.	27	30	33	36	39	42	45	48	51	54
4.	4	8	12	16	20	24	28	32	36	40
5.	20	24	28	32	36	40	44	48	52	56
6.	30	27	24	21	18	15	12	9	6	3
7.	40	36	32	28	24	20	16	12	8	4
8.	32	36	40	44	48	52	56	60	64	68
9.	54	51	48	45	42	39	36	33	30	27
10.	52	48	44	40	36	32	28	24	20	16

Page 51

Properties of number 

Multiples

1. 27 → 30	**2.** 42 → 50	**3.** 56 → 60	**4.** 15 → 20
5. 92 → 100	**6.** 134 → 140	**7.** 7 → 9	**8.** 26 → 27
9. 31 → 33	**10.** 45 → 48	**11.** 17 → 18	**12.** 42 → 45
13. 14 → 15	**14.** 26 → 30	**15.** 31 → 35	**16.** 45 → 50
17. 17 → 20	**18.** 42 → 45	**19.** 6 → 8	**20.** 18 → 20
21. 31 → 32	**22.** 24 → 28	**23.** 37 → 40	**24.** 21 → 24

Photocopy Masters

Page 52

Multiplication/division N22

Sixes

1	2	3	4	5	6	7	8	9	10
11	12	13	14	15	16	17	18	19	20
21	22	23	24	25	26	27	28	29	30
31	32	33	34	35	36	37	38	39	40
41	42	43	44	45	46	47	48	49	50
51	52	53	54	55	56	57	58	59	60
61	62	63	64	65	66	67	68	69	70
71	72	73	74	75	76	77	78	79	80
81	82	83	84	85	86	87	88	89	90
91	92	93	94	95	96	97	98	99	100

Answers will vary.

Page 53

Multiplication/division N22

Threes and sixes

1. 2 x 3 = 6
2. 1 x 6 = 6
3. 4 x 6 = 24
4. 5 x 3 = 15
5. 7 x 3 = 21
6. 5 x 6 = 30
7. 8 x 6 = 48
8. 2 x 6 = 12
9. 8 x 3 = 24
10. 1 x 3 = 3
11. 7 x 6 = 42
12. 10 x 6 = 60
13. 3 x 3 = 9
14. 10 x 3 = 30
15. 9 x 3 = 27
16. 6 x 6 = 36
17. 3 x 6 = 18
18. 4 x 3 = 12
19. 6 x 3 = 18
20. 9 x 6 = 54

Page 55

Multiplication/division N23

Nines

1	2	3	4	5	6	7	8	9	10
11	12	13	14	15	16	17	18	19	20
21	22	23	24	25	26	27	28	29	30
31	32	33	34	35	36	37	38	39	40
41	42	43	44	45	46	47	48	49	50
51	52	53	54	55	56	57	58	59	60
61	62	63	64	65	66	67	68	69	70
71	72	73	74	75	76	77	78	79	80
81	82	83	84	85	86	87	88	89	90
91	92	93	94	95	96	97	98	99	100

Answers will vary.

Page 57

Multiplication/division N23

Patterns in nines

1. 27 **2.** 36 **3.** 18 **4.** 81 **5.** 54 **6.** 72
7. 45 **8.** 54 **9.** 90 **10.** 63 **11.** 27 **12.** 72
13. 81 **14.** 45 **15.** 63 **16.** 36 **17.** 108 **18.** 99

Page 58

Multiplication/division N24

Sevens

1. 2 x 7 = 14 **2.** 5 x 7 = 35 **3.** 1 x 7 = 7 **4.** 6 x 7 = 42
5. 4 x 7 = 28 **6.** 10 x 7 = 70 **7.** 8 x 7 = 56 **8.** 3 x 7 = 21
9. 9 x 7 = 63 **10.** 7 x 7 = 49 **11.** 7 ÷ 7 = 1 **12.** 28 ÷ 7 = 4
13. 42 ÷ 7 = 6 **14.** 70 ÷ 7 = 10 **15.** 21 ÷ 7 = 3 **16.** 49 ÷ 7 = 7
17. 63 ÷ 7 = 9 **18.** 21 ÷ 7 = 3 **19.** 35 ÷ 7 = 5 **20.** 56 ÷ 7 = 8

Photocopy Masters

Page 59

Multiplication/division N24

Sixes and sevens

e 42

Page 60

Multiplication/division N24

Multiplication table

x 1	1	2	3	4	5	6	7	8	9	10
x 2	2	4	6	8	10	12	14	16	18	20
x 3	3	6	9	12	15	18	21	24	27	30
x 4	4	8	12	16	20	24	28	32	36	40
x 5	5	10	15	20	25	30	35	40	45	50
x 6	6	12	18	24	30	36	42	48	54	60
x 7	7	14	21	28	35	42	49	56	63	70
x 8	8	16	24	32	40	48	56	64	72	80
x 9	9	18	27	36	45	54	63	72	81	90
x 10	10	20	30	40	50	60	70	80	90	100

Page 62

Multiplication/division N25

Multiplying and dividing by 10 and 100

1. 17 x 10 = 170
2. 60 ÷ 10 = 6
3. 90 x 10 = 900
4. 140 ÷ 10 = 14
5. 27 x 100 = 2700
6. 8000 ÷ 100 = 80
7. 37 x 100 = 3700
8. 2400 ÷ 100 = 24
9. 42 x 10 = 420
10. 1300 ÷ 100 = 13
11. 250 ÷ 10 = 25
12. 16 x 100 = 1600

Page 63

Multiplication/division 

Multiplying

Answers will vary.

Photocopy Masters

Page 64
Multiplication/division **N26**

Multiplying

1. 3 x 24 = 60 + 12 = 72
2. 4 x 32 = 120 + 8 = 128
3. 5 x 25 = 100 + 25 = 125
4. 4 x 42 = 160 + 8 = 168
5. 6 x 17 = 60 + 42 = 102
6. 2 x 34 = 60 + 8 = 68
7. 5 x 28 = 100 + 40 = 140
8. 6 x 34 = 180 + 24 = 204

Page 65
Fractions/decimals 

Fractions

1. $\frac{1}{4}$ $\frac{3}{4}$
2. $\frac{1}{3}$ $\frac{2}{3}$
3. $\frac{1}{6}$ $\frac{3}{6} = \frac{1}{2}$ $\frac{5}{6}$
4. $\frac{2}{5}$ $\frac{3}{5}$
5. $\frac{1}{8}$ $\frac{3}{8}$ $\frac{5}{8}$ $\frac{6}{8} = \frac{3}{4}$
6. $\frac{3}{10}$ $\frac{4}{10} = \frac{2}{5}$ $\frac{7}{10}$ $\frac{9}{10}$

Page 66
Fractions/decimals **N27**

Ordering fractions

1. $\frac{1}{3} < \frac{1}{2}$
2. $\frac{1}{5} < \frac{1}{4}$
3. $\frac{3}{8} > \frac{1}{4}$
4. $\frac{1}{2} > \frac{2}{5}$
5. $\frac{5}{8} > \frac{1}{2}$
6. $\frac{1}{4} = \frac{2}{8}$
7. $\frac{4}{5} > \frac{4}{6}$
8. $\frac{6}{8} = \frac{3}{4}$
9. $\frac{1}{6} > \frac{1}{8}$
10. $\frac{2}{3} < \frac{3}{4}$
11. $\frac{5}{8} > \frac{3}{5}$
12. $\frac{2}{3} > \frac{1}{3}$
13. $\frac{4}{6} = \frac{2}{3}$
14. $\frac{4}{5} < \frac{7}{8}$
15. $\frac{4}{8} > \frac{2}{5}$

Page 68
Fractions/decimals 

Fractions

1. $\frac{1}{2}$ of 8 = 4
2. $\frac{1}{3}$ of 9 = 3
3. $\frac{1}{4}$ of 12 = 3
4. $\frac{1}{5}$ of 10 = 2
5. $\frac{1}{6}$ of 6 = 1
6. $\frac{1}{8}$ of 8 = 1
7. $\frac{2}{3}$ of 6 = 4
8. $\frac{3}{4}$ of 8 = 6
9. $\frac{2}{5}$ of 10 = 4
10. $\frac{3}{3}$ of 6 = 6
11. $\frac{3}{5}$ of 20 = 12
12. $\frac{1}{2}$ of 12 = 6
13. $\frac{3}{4}$ of 12 = 9
14. $\frac{2}{3}$ of 9 = 6
15. $\frac{4}{5}$ of 15 = 12
16. $\frac{1}{6}$ of 12 = 2
17. $\frac{5}{6}$ of 12 = 10
18. $\frac{1}{4}$ of 16 = 4
19. $\frac{3}{4}$ of 16 = 12
20. $\frac{1}{5}$ of 50 = 10

Photocopy Masters

Page 69

Place-value N29

Rounding

A 424 → 420	B 434 → 430	C 431 → 430	D 421 → 420
E 437 → 440	F 439 → 440	G 425 → 430	H 428 → 430
I 774 → 770	J 766 → 770	K 775 → 780	L 762 → 760
M 778 → 780	N 761 → 760	O 771 → 770	P 770 → 770

Page 71

Place-value N29

Rounding

1. 634
2. 493
3. 346 or 349
4. 639 or 643
5. 934
6. 946
7. 469
8. 396
9. 394
10. 463
11. 936 or 943
12. 693 or 694
13. 649
14. 369
15. 436 or 439
16. 496
17. 364
18. 963 or 964

Page 72

Addition/subtraction N30

Adding

1. 352 + 47 = 399
2. 464 + 28 = 492
3. 537 + 84 = 621
4. 127 + 346 = 473
5. 258 + 463 = 721
6. 725 + 149 = 874
7. 358 + 462 = 820
8. 723 + 159 = 882
9. 271 + 436 = 707
10. 852 + 109 = 961
11. 203 + 598 = 801
12. 438 + 159 = 597

Page 74

Addition/subtraction N30

Adding 3-digit numbers

1. 317 + 503 = 820
2. 174 + 216 = 390
3. 503 + 216 = 719
4. 428 + 503 = 931
5. 317 + 174 = 491
6. 295 + 503 = 798
7. 428 + 174 = 602
8. 428 + 216 = 644
9. 295 + 317 = 612

Page 75

Addition/subtraction N31

Subtracting multiples of 10

1. 82 – 30 = 52
2. 47 – 20 = 27
3. 165 – 50 = 115
4. 258 – 40 = 218

Photocopy Masters

Page 75 cont ...

Addition/subtraction N31

5. 143 – 60 = 83
6. 237 – 70 = 167
7. 425 – 30 = 395
8. 318 – 50 = 268
9. 537 – 70 = 467
10. 108 – 80 = 28
11. 207 – 40 = 167
12. 356 – 70 = 286
13. 423 – 60 = 363
14. 712 – 50 = 662
15. 625 – 90 = 535
16. 839 – 80 = 759
17. 320 – 70 = 250
18. 540 – 80 = 460
19. 817 – 30 = 787
20. 905 – 20 = 885

Page 76

Addition/subtraction N32

Subtracting

1. 134 – 65 = 69
2. 152 – 86 = 66
3. 124 – 77 = 47
4. 186 – 98 = 88
5. 213 – 156 = 57
6. 325 – 178 = 147
7. 232 – 57 = 175
8. 241 – 85 = 156
9. 356 – 178 = 178

Page 77

Addition/subtraction N33

Subtracting

1. 756 – 214 = 542
2. 947 – 323 = 624
3. 685 – 462 = 223
4. 892 – 551 = 341
5. 534 – 322 = 212
6. 383 – 171 = 212
7. 468 – 235 = 233
8. 565 – 443 = 122
9. 276 – 132 = 144
10. 627 – 516 = 111
11. 879 – 364 = 515
12. 754 – 621 = 133

Page 78

Addition/subtraction N33

Subtracting

1. 729 – 387 = 342
2. 638 – 265 = 373
3. 846 – 492 = 354
4. 945 – 573 = 372
5. 534 – 281 = 253
6. 624 – 292 = 332
7. 835 – 382 = 453
8. 719 – 156 = 563

Page 79

Addition/subtraction

Subtracting

Answers will vary.

Photocopy Masters

Page 80

Properties of number **N34**

Odds and evens

1. 75 745 **2.** 54 574 **3.** 74 754 **4.** 45 457

5. 93 963 **6.** 36 396 **7.** 96 936 **8.** 39 369

9. 81 841 **10.** 14 148 **11.** 84 814 **12.** 41 481

Page 81

Properties of number **N34**

Odds and evens

1. odd + odd = even **2.** odd + even = odd

3. even + odd = odd **4.** even + even = even

5. odd – odd = even **6.** even – even = even

7. odd – even = odd **8.** even – odd = odd

9. odd + odd + even = even **10.** even + odd + even = odd

11. odd + even + even = odd **12.** even + even + even = even

13. odd + odd + odd = odd **14.** odd + even + odd = even

15. odd + odd – even = even **16.** even + odd – even = odd

17. odd + even – odd = even **18.** even – odd – even = odd

Page 82

Properties of number **N35**

Negative numbers

1. 10 °C **2.** 2 °C **3.** $^{-}3$ °C **4.** 3 °C **5.** $^{-}6$ °C

6. 3 °C **7.** $^{-}1$ °C **8.** 0 °C **9.** 3 °C **10.** 6 °C

11. $^{-}4$ °C **12.** 7 °C **13.** $^{-}2$ °C **14.** $^{-}18$ °C

Page 83

Multiplication/division **N36**

Doubling

1. 10 + 60 = 70 **2.** 30 + 40 = 70 **3.** 50 + 80 = 130

4. 20 + 140 = 160 **5.** 40 + 100 = 140 **6.** 30 + 160 = 190

7. 50 + 120 = 170 **8.** 40 + 20 = 60

Answers will vary.

Page 84

Multiplication/division **N36**

Halving

Answers will vary.

Photocopy Masters

Page 85

Multiplication/division N36

Doubling and halving

140 → 280
360 → 720
270 → 540
190 → 380
480 → 960
1300 → 2600
2400 → 4800
3600 → 7200
4700 → 9400
1900 → 3800

420 → 210
860 → 430
630 → 315
290 → 145
350 → 175
4200 → 2100
6800 → 3400
2700 → 1350
8500 → 4250
3900 → 1950

Page 86

Multiplication/division N37

Multiplying

1. 25 x 3 = 75
2. 31 x 2 = 62
3. 42 x 4 = 168
4. 24 x 2 = 48
5. 35 x 3 = 105
6. 52 x 4 = 208
7. 54 x 3 = 162
8. 33 x 4 = 132
9. 62 x 5 = 310

Page 87

Multiplication/division 

Multiplying

Answers will vary.

Page 88

Multiplication/division N38

Dividing

1. 16 ÷ 3 = 5 r 1
2. 12 ÷ 5 = 2 r 2
3. 15 ÷ 4 = 3 r 3
4. 17 ÷ 2 = 8 r 1
5. 26 ÷ 6 = 4 r 2
6. 19 ÷ 2 = 9 r 1
7. 30 ÷ 7 = 4 r 2
8. 50 ÷ 9 = 5 r 5
9. 23 ÷ 5 = 4 r 3
10. 26 ÷ 8 = 3 r 2
11. 19 ÷ 4 = 4 r 3
12. 18 ÷ 7 = 2 r 4
13. 16 ÷ 6 = 2 r 4
14. 29 ÷ 3 = 9 r 2
15. 54 ÷ 5 = 10 r 4
16. 38 ÷ 4 = 9 r 2

Page 89

Multiplication/division N38

Problem page

1. 14 ÷ 3 = 4 r 2 — 4 cakes each, 2 left over
2. 50 ÷ 6 = 8 r 2 — 8 stickers
3. 5 x 7 = 35   35 + 3 = 38 — 38 children

Page 89 cont ...

Multiplication/division N38

4. $42 \div 5 = 8$ r 2 — 8 stamps, 2p left
5. $34 \div 6 = 5$ r 4 — 5 full boxes
6. $30 \div 4 = 7$ r 2 — 8 boats
7. 23
8. 4, 11, 22 or 44

Page 90

Multiplication/division N39

Dividing

1. $2\overline{)34} = 17$
2. $3\overline{)42} = 14$
3. $4\overline{)56} = 14$
4. $5\overline{)75} = 15$
5. $6\overline{)84} = 14$
6. $3\overline{)51} = 17$
7. $2\overline{)46} = 23$
8. $4\overline{)68} = 17$
9. $8\overline{)96} = 12$
10. $7\overline{)84} = 12$
11. $3\overline{)72} = 24$
12. $4\overline{)88} = 22$

Page 91

Fractions/decimals N40

Tenths

1. $2\frac{2}{10}$ and 2·2
2. $1\frac{4}{10}$ and 1·4
3. $3\frac{7}{10}$ and 3·7
4. $1\frac{9}{10}$ and 1·9
5. $2\frac{5}{10}$ and 2·5
6. $\frac{6}{10}$ and 0·6
7. $3\frac{2}{10}$ and 3·2
8. $2\frac{1}{10}$ and 2·1
9. $1\frac{2}{10}$ and 1·2
10. $3\frac{5}{10}$ and 3·5

Page 92

Fractions/decimals N40

Tenths

$1{\cdot}3 = 1\frac{3}{10}$ $\frac{5}{10} = 0{\cdot}5$ $2\frac{4}{10} = 2{\cdot}4$ $0{\cdot}9 = \frac{9}{10}$ $3\frac{5}{10} = 3{\cdot}5$

$4{\cdot}3 = 4\frac{3}{10}$ $1{\cdot}7 = 1\frac{7}{10}$ $1\frac{1}{10} = 1{\cdot}1$ $3{\cdot}6 = 3\frac{6}{10}$

0·5, 0·9, 1·1, 1·3, 1·7, 2·4, 3·5, 3·6, 4·3

Page 93

Fractions/decimals N40

Tenths

1. E
2. D
3. H
4. B
5. G
6. A
7. K
8. J
9. C
10. I
11. L
12. F

Page 94

Fractions/decimals **N41**

Hundredths

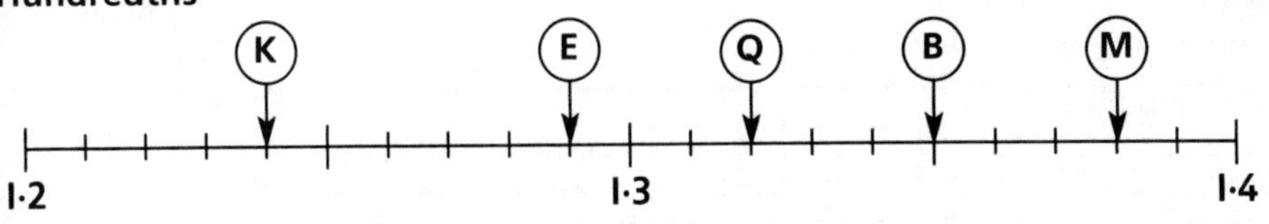

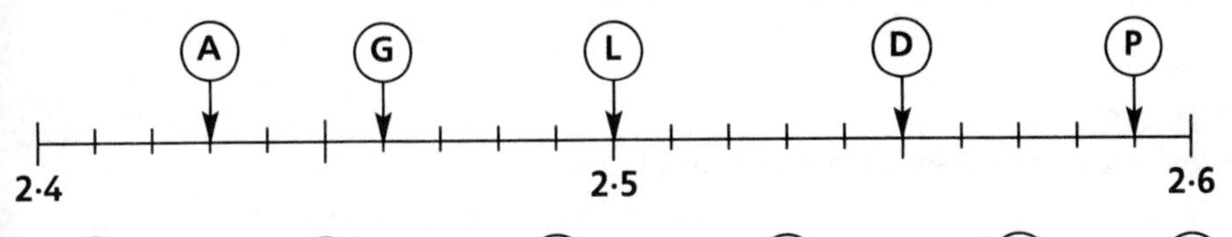

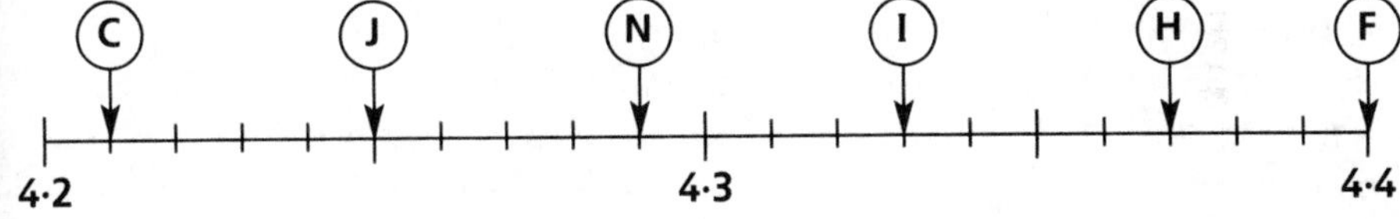

Page 95

Fractions/decimals **N41**

Hundredths

1. £1·22 **2.** £3·15 **3.** £0·91 **4.** £4·50 **5.** £2·72 **6.** £1·55
7. £3·51 **8.** £1·10 **9.** £2·01 **10.** £6·25 **11.** £5·54 **12.** £10·07

Page 96

Addition/subtraction **N42**

Subtracting

1. 762 – 219 = 543 **2.** 384 – 168 = 216 **3.** 686 – 159 = 527
4. 943 – 536 = 407 **5.** 471 – 324 = 147 **6.** 565 – 257 = 308
7. 837 – 418 = 419 **8.** 572 – 445 = 127

Page 97

Addition/subtraction **N43**

Adding and subtracting decimals

1. £2·30 + £1·60 = £3·90 **2.** £4·50 + £2·30 = £6·80
3. £4·50 + £4·25 = £8·75 **4.** £5·45 + £1·85 = £7·30
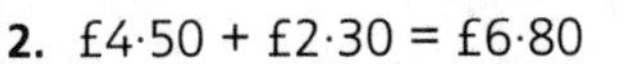
5. £2·30 + £3·75 = £6·05 **6.** £4·50 + £1·85 = £6·35
7. £4·50 – £2·30 = £2·20 **8.** £2·30 – £1·60 = £0·70
9. £5·45 – £4·50 = £0·95 **10.** £4·25 – £1·85 = £2·40
11. £3·75 – £2·30 = £1·45 **12.** £4·50 – £4·25 = £0·25

Photocopy Masters

Page 98

Length M1

Centimetres

Estimates will vary.

a	b	c	d	e	f	g	h
16 cm	12 cm	17 cm	3 cm	4 cm	10 cm	4 cm	15 cm

Page 99

Length M1

Millimetres, centimetres, metres and kilometres

1. 1 cm= 10 mm
2. 1 cm 7 mm = 17mm
3. $\frac{1}{2}$ cm = 5 mm
4. 5 cm = 50 mm
5. 3 cm = 35 mm
6. 1 m = 1000mm
7. 1 m = 100 cm
8. 1m 20 cm = 120 cm
9. 60 mm = 6 cm
10. $\frac{1}{4}$ m = 25 cm
11. 35 mm = 3·5 cm
12. 2m 50cm = 250 cm
13. 100 cm = 1 m
14. 1 km = 1000 m
15. 600 cm = 6 m
16. 1000 cm = 10 m
17. $\frac{1}{2}$ km = 500 m
18. 1000 mm = 1m
19. 1000 m = 1 km
20. 2000 m = 2 km
21. 1500 m = 1·5 km
22. 10 000 m = 10 km

Page 100

Weight M2

Grams and kilograms

1. 1 kg = 1000 g
2. 2 kg = 2000 g
3. 7 kg = 7000 g
4. 10 kg = 10 000 g
5. $1\frac{1}{2}$ kg = 1500 g
6. $5\frac{1}{2}$ kg = 5500 g
7. 1 kg 600 g = 1600 g
8. 2 kg 420 g = 2420 g
9. 3 kg 560 g = 3560 g
10. 7 kg 180 g = 7180 g
11. 1100 g = 1 kg 100 g
12. 3000 g = 3 kg 0 g
13. 2600 g = 2 kg 600 g
14. 4300 g = 4 kg 300 g
15. 2150 g = 2 kg 150 g
16. 1850 g = 1 kg 850 g
17. 4635 g = 4 kg 635 g
18. 2742 g = 2 kg 742 g
19. 1803 g = 1 kg 803 g
20. 1045 g = 1 kg 45 g

Photocopy Masters

Page 101

Capacity M3

Litres and millilitres

1. 1000 ml = 1 l
2. 3000 ml = 3 l
3. 500 ml = 0·5 l
4. 7500 ml = 7·5 l
5. 1 l = 1000 ml
6. $\frac{1}{2}$ l = 500 ml
7. 2 l 300 ml = 2300 ml
8. $\frac{1}{10}$ l = 100 ml
9. 1 l = 2 pints
10. 2 l = 4 pints
11. 500 ml = 1 pint
12. 3500 ml = 7 pints
13. 2 pints = 1 l
14. 16 pints = 8 l
15. $\frac{1}{2}$ pint = $\frac{1}{4}$ l = 250 ml
16. 7 pints = $3\frac{1}{2}$ l

Page 102

Area 

Area

1. 15 squares
2. 16 squares largest area
3. 12 squares
4. 14 squares
5. 14 squares
6. 12 squares
7. 15 squares
8. 14 squares
9. 14 squares
10. 11 squares smallest area

Page 103

Area M4

Area

1. 16 cm^2
2. 14 cm^2
3. 18 cm^2
4. 12 cm^2
5. 25 cm^2
6. 28 cm^2
7. 36 cm^2
8. 35 cm^2
9. 12 cm^2
10. 12 cm^2

Page 104

Perimeter 

Perimeter and area

	a	b	c	d	e	f	g	h	i	j	k
Perimeter cm	10	16	16	10	14	14	8	10	14	24	20
area cm^2	6	16	15	4	8	10	4	4	10	36	25

Page 105

Perimeter M5

Perimeter and area

Answers will vary.

Photocopy Masters

Page 106

Time **M6**

Telling the time

1. 3:10	**2.** 4:15	**3.** 5:55	**4.** 3:26
5. 7:48	**6.** 9:31	**7.** 7:44	**8.** 2:52
9. 11:27	**10.** 6:03	**11.** 3:38	**12.** 10:09

Page 107

Time **M6**

Telling the time

1

2 03:50

3

4

5 07:21

6

7 10:36

8

9

10

11

12

Page 108

Time 

Calendars

April						
M	**Tu**	**W**	**Th**	**F**	**Sa**	**Su**
		1	2	3	4	5
6	7	8	9	10	11	12
13	14	15	16	17	18	19
20	21	22	23	24	25	26
27	28	29	30			

May						
M	**Tu**	**W**	**Th**	**F**	**Sa**	**Su**
				1	2	3
4	5	6	7	8	9	10
11	12	13	14	15	16	17
18	19	20	21	22	23	24
25	26	27	28	29	30	31

Page 108 cont ...

Time M7

June						
M	Tu	W	Th	F	Sa	Su
1	2	3	4	5	6	7
8	9	10	11	12	13	14
15	16	17	18	19	20	21
22	23	24	25	26	27	28
29	30					

July						
M	Tu	W	Th	F	Sa	Su
		1	2	3	4	5
6	7	8	9	10	11	12
13	14	15	16	17	18	19
20	21	22	23	24	25	26
27	28	29	30	31		

Page 109

Time M7

Calendars

1. Sunday
2. Tuesday
3. Monday
4. Wednesday
5. Tuesday
6. Thursday
7. Tuesday
8. Sunday
9. Friday
10. Wednesday
11. Friday
12. Thursday
13. Thursday
14. Monday
15. Tuesday
16. Sunday

Page 110

Time M8

Timetable

1. 7 minutes
2. 18 minutes
3. 46 minutes
4. 68 minutes
5. 25 minutes
6. 55 minutes
7. 77 minutes
8. 61 minutes
9. 18 minutes
10. 22 minutes
11. 37 minutes
12. 22 minutes
13. 21 minutes
14. 43 minutes

Page 111

Time M9

Minutes and seconds

1. 65 seconds
2. 85 seconds
3. 120 seconds
4. 130 seconds
5. 185 seconds
6. 90 seconds
7. 150 seconds
8. 600 seconds
9. 1 minute 15 seconds
10. 1 minute 30 seconds
11. 1 minute 8 seconds
12. 1 minute 40 seconds
13. 2 minutes 0 seconds
14. 3 minutes 20 seconds

Photocopy Masters

Page 112

2-d shape **S1**

Polygons

1. rectangle
2. equilateral triangle
3. regular hexagon
4. pentagon
5. triangle
6. hexagon
7. pentagon
8. pentagon
9. hexagon

Page 113

2-d shape **S2**

Regular polygons

1. equilateral triangle
2. square
3. regular hexagon
4. regular octagon
5. regular heptagon
6. regular pentagon

Page 114

2-d shape **S2**

Isosceles triangles

1. 2. 3. 4. 5.

6.

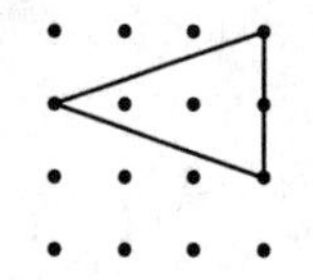

7. 8. 9.

Page 115

Symmetry **S3**

Symmetry

1.

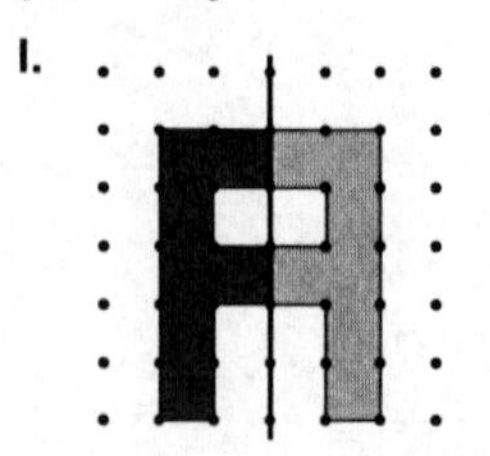

2. 3.

4.–9. Answers will vary.

Photocopy Masters

Page 122

Position **S7**

Coordinates

1. (3,2) **2.** (5,0) **3.** (7,6) **4.** (4,7) **5.** (2,5)
6. (1,1) **7.** (8,3) **8.** (4,4) **9.** (1,7) **10.** (0,5)

Page 123

Frequency tables **D1**

Frequency tables

digit	0	1	2	3	4	5	6	7	8	9
frequency	= 3	= 5	= 11	= 9	= 8	= 10	= 6	= 8	= 7	= 5

Page 124

Pictographs **D2**

Pictographs

1. 14 days **2.** 16 days **3.** 9 days **4.** 19 days
5. July **6.** May **7.** 3 days **8.** 5 days
9. 7 days **10.** 5 days **11.** 12 days **12.** 16 days
13. 15 days **14.** 22 days

Page 125

Bar graphs **D3**

Bar graphs

1. 30 children **2.** 29 children **3.** 26 children **4.** 30 children
5. 29 children **6.** 27 children **7.** 24 children **8.** 27 children
9. Y4 **10.** Y4 **11.** Y5 **12.** Y4
13. 5 children **14.** 2 children **15.** 5 children **16.** 3 children

Page 126

Sorting diagrams **D4**

Venn diagrams

1.

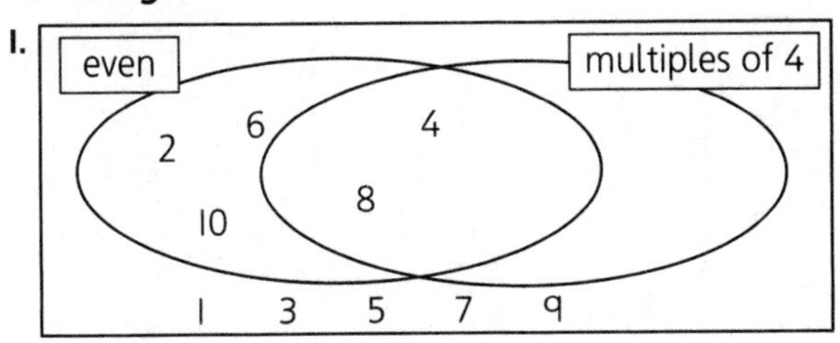

Page 126 cont ...

2.

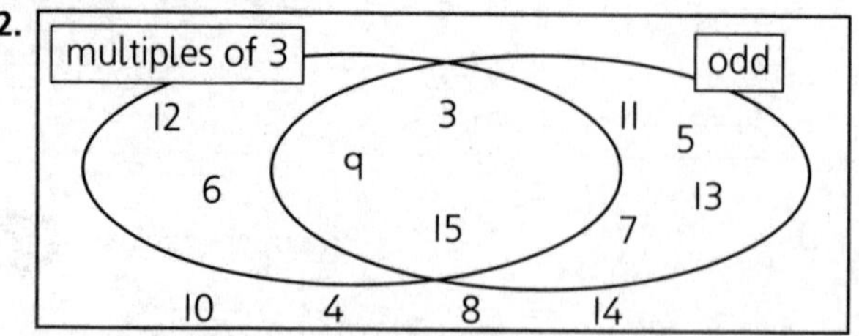

3.

multiples of 2
multiples of 3
8
14
2
4
6
12
3
15
9
13
5

Page 127

Carroll diagrams

1.

	even	odd
multiple of 3	6 12	3 9
not a multiple of 3	8 2 4 10	1 7 5

2.

	factor of 4	not a factor of 4
multiple of 2	2 4	14 10 8 16 12 6 18
not a multiple of 2		9 13 15

3.

	digit total less than 10	digit total not less than 10
even	26 52 40	38 66 76 28
odd	15 17 63 45	77 85